Fred T. Loomis

PILOT'S VIEW WHEN TAKING OFF AT ELMIRA

FLIGHT WITHOUT POWER

The Art of Gliding and Soaring

By

LEWIN R. BARRINGER

PITMAN PUBLISHING CORPORATION

NEW YORK   CHICAGO

TL
760
B27F

ASSOCIATED COMPANIES

SIR ISAAC PITMAN & SONS, Ltd.
Bath · London · Melbourne · Johannesburg · Singapore

SIR ISAAC PITMAN & SONS (CANADA), Ltd.
381-383 Church Street, Toronto

Advisory Editor
Professor Alexander Klemin
DANIEL GUGGENHEIM SCHOOL OF AERONAUTICS
COLLEGE OF ENGINEERING, NEW YORK UNIVERSITY

PRINTED IN THE UNITED STATES OF AMERICA

FOREWORD

During the two years after my first taste of motorless flying in 1930, I operated the Wings Gliding School near Philadelphia which trained over sixty students largely by methods that my associates and I had to devise due to lack of any adequate book or manual on the subject. Following my introduction to high performance soaring by my friend Richard du Pont in the summer of 1934, I frequently encountered conditions and had experiences in flight the correct explanation of which also could not be found in any book yet published.

Many times during the past two years as editor of *Soaring* and manager of The Soaring Society of America I felt an increasing need for an up-to-date, authoritative book covering all phases of motorless flying. Although several excellent books have been written, soaring technique and sailplane design have advanced so rapidly in recent years that these are now inadequate. An indication of this progress is the fact that while making several thousand flights at Wings Field eight years ago we never suspected possibilities of soaring over this field which is situated in level country. Now the members of a soaring club are being taught not only how to win their "C" licenses but also how to go on to high performance soaring on thermal upcurrents in this same part of the country. From being restricted to a few isolated sites in the mountains, soaring can now be done from large fields situated nearly anywhere in the country.

So it was that when approached to write this book I well knew the great need for such a work but also realized that to be truly authoritative certain chapters should be written by recognized experts in their particular fields. I wish to express my appreciation for the invaluable co-operation of my co-authors. H. Randers-Pehrson is a recognized authority in the historical field and a member of the staff of the Division of Aeronautics of the Library of Congress, Washington, D. C. Paul and Ernest Schweizer of Elmira, N. Y., are leading glider designers and builders who pioneered all-metal construction in this field. Karl O. Lange, an eminent meteorologist connected with the Blue Hill Meteorological Observatory of Harvard University, is also a former soaring pilot, Contest

Director for The Soaring Society of America and designer of one of the first successful radio-meteorgraphs. Charles O. Colvin is a well-known expert in the field of aircraft instruments.

In expressing my thanks and gratitude to those who have assisted me I wish particularly to mention Milton Stoughton for his initial work on the aerodynamics of gliding flight; Fred C. Barnes, John Robinson, Gilbert Walters, Gustave Scheurer, and Amos Wood for their information on the soaring sites at Tejon Ranch, Torrey Pines Mesa, Altamount Pass, Schley Field, and Steptoe Butte, respectively; Jay Buxton for help on technical details of launching methods used in California; A. Ivanoff, British "Silver C" pilot, for his suggestion that English data and statistics be included; The Soaring Society of America for permission to reprint certain passages published in *Soaring;* and all those who helped so much by supplying photographs for illustrations.

It is my sincere hope that this book may help to promote the soaring movement.

LEWIN B. BARRINGER

Llewellyn Park
Orange, N. J.

CONTENTS

CHAPTER I

HISTORY OF MOTORLESS FLIGHT

By N. H. Randers-Pehrson

T HE EARLY HISTORY OF AVIATION is a history of failures and frustrations because, not realizing the possibilities of gliding and soaring, men tried to fly by muscular power and spent their time and ingenuity on futile wing-flapping devices. Later when this method had been discredited, practical progress was retarded by the false belief that an engine is indispensable for human flight.

The foundation for scientific study of aviation was laid by Sir George Cayley who in the beginning of the nineteenth century made the first attempts to explain mathematically the principles of flight. He also experimented with glider models, and built a large machine which, although provided with some kind of propelling mechanism, was tried in gliding flight. When launched from a hill-top without a pilot, it would sail with perfect balance to the plain below, and when a person ran with it against the wind, it would sometimes carry him a few yards. Probably Cayley had the knowledge and ability to build and operate a man-carrying glider, but unfortunately he had his mind set upon the need for an engine and so missed the opportunity of becoming the father of motorless flight. He was followed by a number of gifted and enthusiastic workers, mostly in England and France, who made valuable theoretical contributions but achieved no practical results because they also were striving for power flight. Among the few who favored motorless flight was Captain Le Bris, a French sailor who used the albatross as a pattern for a glider. With this he was towed into the air like a kite in 1855, and again with a second Albatross in 1867, but mishaps and lack of funds brought the experiments to an end. Le Bris' glider had streamline form and a large aspect ratio; the angle of incidence of the wings could be varied in flight. There was also Louis Pierre Mouillard, a Frenchman who lived in Algeria and who spent all his spare time studying those masters of soaring flight, the great vultures. Mouillard described his observations in a book entitled *L'Empire de l'Air*, a work which furnished much inspiration to others, but his own attempts to make wings for gliding were crude and ineffectual.

Otto Lilienthal was the first man to learn the art of flight from the birds, to practice the art himself, and to give it to humanity. From boyhood he and his brother Gustav watched the birds, especially the storks, so abundant near their home in Pomerania. After years of study and aerodynamic experiments he produced the best treatise on the theory of flight that had yet appeared. The next step was to learn to fly. Lack of a suitable engine had been a stumbling block for other inventors, but Lilienthal concluded that an engine was not necessary or even desirable for pioneer flying. In 1891 he made his first glider of peeled willow rods covered with waxed fabric; it was shaped like a pair of broad bird's wings and had fixed horizontal and vertical tail surfaces. During the next five years he built several hang gliders, both monoplanes and biplanes. To operate these, the pilot stood in the middle of the apparatus, thrusting his arms through padded openings in the frame, so that the weight in flight rested on his elbows. He maintained his balance in the air by moving his body or swinging his legs to shift the center of gravity and keep it directly under the center of lift. This required great acrobatic ability, but by persistent practice Lilienthal mastered the art and became so skillful that he could fly even in strong winds. He was, however, aware of the need for a better system of control, and on one of his last gliders used a movable elevator. Lilienthal made his first flights from a springboard in his garden, then from low hills in the neighborhood, and finally he built an artificial hill 50 feet high, with a shed for the gliders in the top. He also found a suitable gliding site at Rhinow, where there are low mountains covered with heath and grass. Here his flights became longer, up to 900 feet, and he succeeded in making turns, sometimes of almost 180°. It was at Rhinow on August 9, 1896, that he lost his balance in the air, fell and was fatally injured. It was Lilienthal's hope that others would take up gliding as a sport. Therefore he published detailed reports of his activities and did not object to the hundreds of spectators who flocked to his flying hill every Sunday. The following he had wished for was slow in coming, but his work was continued by a few capable disciples, notably Pilcher in England, Ferber in France, and Chanute, Herring and the Wright brothers in America.

Percy S. Pilcher built several gliders with slight improvements over Lilienthal's; he launched himself by running downhill, but later used a towline pulled by boys or horses. An accident ended his life in 1899 when he consented to make a flight in unfavorable weather, in order not to disappoint friends who had come to see him fly.

Of greater importance was the work of Octave Chanute, an American civil engineer who for several years had studied the problem of flight and had written a critical history of aviation experiments. Too old to do any flying himself, he hired several younger assistants, among them A. M. Herring, who had previously built and flown a Lilienthal glider. In the summer of 1896 they established a glider camp in the dune region on the southern shore of Lake Michigan. First they tried the Lilienthal glider, which they found dangerous and difficult to handle. The purpose of Chanute's work was to discover better means of control than that of shifting the weight of the pilot, and also to obtain some measure of automatic stability. So he designed a multiplane with wings that could swerve fore and aft to adjust the center of lift; it underwent gradual modifications until quite satisfactory flights could be made. Finally Chanute designed a biplane which later became famous as the "Chanute type," and the ancestor of the first successful powered airplanes. The two cambered lifting surfaces were straight from tip to tip, and trussed together by a girder of vertical struts and diagonal wires, known as a "Pratt truss." This construction was simple and light but very strong; weighing only 23 pounds, it carried 178 pounds. The tail was flexibly attached, an invention of Herring's which improved longitudinal stability; otherwise control was obtained by throwing the legs left and right, but much less strenuous motions were required than with the Lilienthal glider. More than a thousand flights were made without the slightest accident during 1896 and 1897. The glider was manageable in winds up to 31 m.p.h., and sometimes was lifted higher than the starting point. Most of the flights were made straight downhill, but Herring also learned to make a turn and glide lengthwise along the hill, taking advantage of the slope wind. He reported a flight of 927 feet in 48 seconds made in this manner. Among the others who started gliding during Lilienthal's lifetime was a group of young men at Schenectady, New York, who in 1894 formed the first glider club in the world, the "Mohawk Aerial Navigation Company," under the leadership of Charles P. Steinmetz.

Newspaper notices of Lilienthal's death inspired Orville and Wilbur Wright to study the problem of flight. They decided that the method of balancing a glider by shifting the weight of the pilot, as practiced by Lilienthal and Chanute, was not effective and not the method used by birds. Taking the Chanute biplane as model for their designs, they made several important changes. To reduce drag the pilot was placed prone on the lower surface, the tail was discarded and a front elevator used instead; but most important of all, they invented a method of warping the wings for lateral balance. At Kitty Hawk, North Carolina, the Wright brothers made their first tests in the fall of 1900. Only a few flights were made, just enough to prove the soundness of their theories and the effectiveness of the control mechanism. The following year, with a second glider, they made a number of good flights. Chanute, who was a visitor in the camp, said that they had done better than anyone before, but the brothers were disappointed. The performance was not up to expectations, and to secure reliable aerodynamic data for future designs they built a small wind tunnel in which they carried on tests during the winter.

The 1902 glider, with a span of 32 feet and weighing 116 pounds, was a larger machine than anyone had dared try before. It was provided with a fixed vertical tail in addition to the elevator and wing warping device. During September and October 1902 the Wrights made nearly a thousand flights with this glider, improving it according to experience obtained in the air. First they practiced with the elevator alone, then the warping wires were taken into use. The operation of two different controls at the same time caused confusion, but was mastered. Then the glider showed a tendency to side-slip in the turns, and this was remedied by making the vertical tail into a movable rudder. The control of three things at once seemed too complicated, but was simplified by connecting the rudder to the warping wires, since both were intended to be operated together. They now had effective control of their glider and could really begin to learn the pilot's art by continuous practice. The longest flight was 622 feet and lasted 26 seconds. They did not try to set records because the purpose of their work was research rather than spectacular performance. On returning to Dayton they immediately began work on a powered airplane, for which they had to build their own motor. In September 1903 they went to Kitty Hawk again and divided their time there between work on the power "flyer" and practicing with last year's glider. In gliding they now became experts, making many flights of more than half a minute's duration, the longest one lasting 43 seconds. Sometimes they succeeded in hovering in the strong slope wind over one spot, once as long as 26 seconds. With the first flights on the motor flyer, December 17, 1903, the gliding days of the Wright brothers were ended for a long time.

Chanute, who had continued his experiments to obtain automatic stability, ended his active work after sending one of his former assistants, William Avery, with a Chanute glider to the St. Louis Fair in 1904. Avery was the first to use a winch for launching; he was towed from level ground up to 70 feet in the air. His best flights were less than 300 feet from the point where the hook was released, because the field was too small. On the first flight in a better location the towrope snapped and Avery fell and sprained an ankle.

Another American pioneer of motorless flight was J. J. Montgomery of Santa Clara, California. His work had begun in 1883, but not much was known about it before 1905, when he gave exhibitions, launching gliders from hot-air balloons at a height of 4000 feet. The Montgomery gliders had tandem wings which could be warped for steering and balance. The flights lasted up to 20 minutes and included spectacular maneuvering. These exhibitions ended when one of the operators, a professional parachute jumper, crashed and was killed due to the breaking of a stay wire.

The work of the Wright brothers was followed with great interest in France, where Ferdinand Ferber had been working with gliders since 1898. Ferber, Ernest Archdeacon, Gabriel Voisin and others were spurred on by Chanute's reports of the American achievements, which they tried to imitate with indifferent results. The only fact worthy of notice is that they tried the first auto tow, in 1906.

With the development of powered airplanes, motorless flight was all but forgotten. Gliders were built, mostly after the designs of Chanute and Lilienthal, but no advance was made over the achievements of these pioneers, and the interest in gliding as a sport soon petered out. Valuable work was done by José Weiss in England and Igo Etrich in Austria, who used gliders for the study of automatic stability, but this was mainly for the benefit of powerplane design. Orville Wright returned to motorless flight for a short time, but only for the purpose of testing a new stabilizing device intended for airplanes. In October 1911, at his old flying ground at Kitty Hawk, he soared 9 minutes, 45 seconds, setting a record which was not surpassed for ten years. This created a brief revival of interest in gliding, and some of the leaders in the modern soaring movement in America made their first flights in home-made hang gliders at that time.

In Germany Lilienthal's heritage was taken up in 1909 by a group of schoolboys in Darmstadt. Like many other youngsters, they used bedsheets and broomsticks to build primitive gliders, but unlike others, this group held together until broken up by the World War. As the boys grew older and some of them became students at the Technical Institute, their theoretical understanding increased and their designs improved. In 1912 during summer vacation they discovered a wonderful site for motorless flying, on the Wasserkuppe in the Rhön mountains. Here Hans Gutermuth made a flight of 2700 feet, lasting 1 minute, 52 seconds.

The World War interrupted all aviation activity other than military. The airplane was perfected as a weapon, but adaptation to military needs made it unsuited for the purposes of peace: it was dangerous for sport and uneconomical for commerce. After the war Oscar Ursinus, editor of the German magazine *Flugsport,* started a campaign for the development of civil airplanes based on sound aerodynamic design rather than on the brute force of excessive engine power. Remembering the Darmstadt schoolboys, he proposed

Brown Brothers

THE FIRST SOARING FLIGHT
Orville Wright at Kitty Hawk in 1911

a gliding and soaring meet in the Rhön mountains, for the purpose of scientific research and healthful sport. Added interest in motorless flight resulted from the restrictions imposed by the Allies upon powered airplanes in Germany.

The first Rhön competition took place from July to September 1920. Among those who gathered on the Wasserkuppe were engineers and scientists as well as amateurs and former war pilots eager to find a way of satisfying their desire to fly. The combination of science and sport has characterized the movement ever since. Some of the gliders were modeled after motorplanes, others were hang gliders of the Lilienthal and Chanute types. The results were only fair, until towards the end of the meet Wolfgang Klemperer arrived with his cantilever monoplane glider "Schwarzer Teufel," designed by him and built at the Institute of Technology in Aachen. Klemperer used, for the first time, the shock-cord method of launching, and surpassed all competitors by remaining in the air for 2 minutes, 23 seconds, covering more than a mile.

Longer flights were made the following year, when Orville Wright's record was beaten by Klemperer with a flight of 13 minutes; this was surpassed by Arthur Martens, who flew for 15½ minutes on the "Vampyr," and later Friedrich Hart, whose gliding experiments started before the war, raised the record to 21½ minutes. But it was in the third Rhön meeting, in 1922, that things really began to happen. Downhill coasting was now child's play, and the experienced pilots set out to master the art of soaring. Klemperer's "Schwarzer Teufel" had shown the right direction in design, and

WOLFGANG KLEMPERER LANDING HIS "BLUE MOUSE" IN 1921

the "Vampyr," designed and built by professors and students at the Technical Institute in Hannover, was the first true sailplane. On it Martens made the first motorless flight of more than 1 hour, on August 10; the next day Henzen remained in the air for 2 hours, and five days later for more than 3 hours.

Until then motorless flight had attracted little attention outside the small group of devotees, but these achievements demonstrated its possibilities to the whole world. A successful soaring meet was held in September the same year at Itford Hill in England, and during 1923 there were meets at Biskra, Algeria, at Vauville, France, and also on the Crimean peninsula in Russia. The French pilots were, for awhile, serious contenders for first honors: in January 1923 Thoret soared a powerplane with the engine shut off for 7 hours, and this was surpassed first by Maneyrol, then by Barbot, who held the duration of over 8½ hours at the end of the year. The greatest height—1750 feet—was also reached by a Frenchman,

Deschamps, at Biskra. In Germany a new soaring center was established at Rossitten in East Prussia, where sand dunes along the Baltic coast provided favorable conditions. At Rhön permanent buildings began to appear and gliding schools were opened. During the next few years records were constantly bettered, until in 1925 Ferdinand Schulz made the first motorless flight of 12 hours' duration while the distance record had been increased to 15¼ miles. However, nothing new had been learned since 1922. A skilled pilot could soar above a hillside as long as his strength and the slope wind lasted,

Wolfgang Klemperer

THE "VAMPYR" FLYING AT HANNOVER, GERMANY, IN 1921
(Now in Deutches Museum, Munich)

but this was not enough to keep the interest alive. The question was "What next?"

The 1926 Rhön meeting indicated the answer. First Schulz put an end to the notion that soaring was a fair-weather sport, by flying in hail and rain. Then Max Kegel was sucked up by a thunderstorm to a greater height than any motorless plane had reached before, and he more than doubled the distance record from the previous year. At the same meeting Johannes Nehring in the Darmstadt sailplane made a goal flight to the Milseburg and back;

it was much shorter than the record, but of great importance because it was the result of close study of the topographical conditions and air currents. Later, under the supervision of Professor Georgii, Nehring made a number of research flights in very light winds, and during the following year in upcurrents caused by houses and trees. These efforts to explore new possibilities for soaring flight were promoted by the research institute of the Rhön-Rossitten Gesellschaft of which Georgii was the director.

Another important advance was made in 1928, with the beginning of cloud soaring. The fact that upwinds exist under cumulus clouds had been known to meteorologists for some time, and Nehring, flying a light motorplane, had investigated these upwinds. Robert Kronfeld, a young Austrian, was the first to make use of this knowledge when he made contact with a cloud over Wasserkuppe, was lifted 1400 feet, flew with it to Himmeldankberg, where he hung in the slope wind until he could make contact with other clouds and by their help return to the starting point. In the following year cloud soaring became common practice, and the records for distance and height mounted rapidly. Kronfeld now made his second great contribution to the technique of motorless flight by demonstrating storm-front soaring. Kegel had been carried aloft accidentally by a thundercloud, but Kronfeld set out deliberately to explore this possibility for soaring. On July 20, 1929, he started from the Wasserkuppe in the face of a thunderstorm and established a distance record of 85.5 miles and an altitude record of 7525 feet.

The widespread interest in motorless flight awakened by the first sensational demonstrations in 1922 did not last long. Outside of Germany the movement came almost to a standstill, and even in Germany it had some lean years, but the great progress since 1926 brought new life. By 1930 soaring societies were active in many countries, and in that year the ISTUS was organized—the International Association for the Study of Motorless Flight.

In the United States, the land of Lilienthal's foremost disciples, Chanute and the Wright brothers, motorless flight was introduced again in 1928 by a group of German pilots. They brought with them the first modern soaring plane seen in this country, the "Darmstadt," and with it Peter Hesselbach made a flight of over 4 hours on Cape Cod. A glider camp was organized and a wave of enthusiasm for motorless flight swept the country. Unfortunately much of the fervent gliding activity which followed was haphazard and ill-advised, but valuable pioneering work was also done. Even in this early period Americans were not mere imitators of the Germans, but worked out their own methods. At the University of Michigan Professor R. E. Franklin developed the Franklin utility glider and introduced auto-tow training and launching. Franklin also practiced airplane tow, first demonstrated by Espenlaub at the Wasserkuppe in 1926, and in 1930 Frank Hawks was towed across the continent in a Franklin glider (now in Smithsonian Museum, Washington, D. C.). Another spectacular feat of that year was Ralph Barnaby's gliding flight from the airship "Los Angeles."

Outstanding among American soaring pioneers was Hawley Bowlus. He had built his first hang glider in 1911, and now began designing and building modern sailplanes. In October 1929 Bowlus made the first motorless flight of over an hour in an American-built craft, at Point Loma, California; by February 1930 he had raised the American record to over 9 hours, and on April 29-30 his assistant Jack Barstow set an unofficial world record of over 15 hours. An American distance record of 15.7 miles was established in 1929 by Wolfgang Klemperer, famous from the first Rhön meetings. He had come to America as an engineer for the Goodyear Zeppelin Company, and founded a soaring group at Akron, Ohio.

The first soaring meet in America was held in 1930 at Elmira, New York, a site which first was explored by Klemperer and Jack O'Meara. Here, on October 4, Wolf Hirth made the first long thermal flight, 54 miles without the aid of slope winds or clouds. With this flight began the systematic study of thermal currents and the development of thermal soaring technique. Results were evident already in the twelfth Rhön meeting, 1931, when Hirth, Groenhoff and Kronfeld made flights of over 100 kilometers (62 miles) by this method. Flights were also made in the thermal upcurrents created by great cities—over Berlin, Munich and London and by Jack O'Meara over New York.

The mastery of thermal soaring liberated motorless flight from its dependence upon mountains and slopes or chance clouds and storm fronts. Starting from level country became possible by the use of new launching methods: airplane tow, first practiced for exhibition purposes, was perfected as a starting method by Peter Riedel and Günther Groenhoff in Germany, auto tow developed in America, was later brought to Europe, and winch launching was introduced by Kronfeld.

Airplane tow to 6000 feet made possible Kronfeld's glide across the English Channel in 1931, which stimulated interest in motorless flight and brought new life to the movement in Great Britain. The longest flight of the year, Groenhoff's 170-mile storm-front flight from Munich to Kaaden in Czechoslovakia, also started with airplane launching from level ground. It was unsurpassed for three years, but was not an official record because this method of launching was not then recognized. Before the end of the year the official duration record, which had been standing at a little over 14 hours since 1927, was beaten by Lt. William Cocke who soared for almost 22 hours over Honolulu on December 17-18. Cocke's record was at the time considered unbreakable; still it was broken in 1933 by Kurt Schmidt with a flight of 36 hours, 35 minutes.

In the course of a scientific soaring expedition to Brazil, the altitude record which had been standing since 1929 was beaten by

Fred T. Loomis

WARREN E. EATON

Heini Dittmar in February 1934 when he soared to more than 14,000 feet through three layers of towering cumulus clouds near Rio de Janeiro. On the same occasion Hanna Reitsch set a record for women of 7,040 feet. She already held the duration record of 10 hours, and shortly afterwards gained the distance record with a flight of 160 kilometers.

In the United States The Soaring Society of America was formed in 1932 and under the leadership of Warren Eaton a sound and well-organized soaring movement replaced the early over-enthusiasm. America offers excellent natural advantages for motorless flight, good conditions for thermal soaring and long mountain ridges for slope soaring. Soon American pilots acquired sufficient skill to utilize these advantages. In 1932 Jack O'Meara set an American record of 66 miles; in 1933 Richard du Pont soared 122 miles along the Blue Ridge, and in 1934 he surpassed the world record with a cloud flight of 158 miles. Lewin Barringer's flight from Ellenville, New York, to Piketown, Pennsylvania, in April the following year was 3 miles shorter, but notable as the longest slope-wind flight ever made.

In Germany the 1934 Rhön meeting brought a surprise: Groenhoff's three year, unofficial distance record was surpassed four times in two days, Heini Dittmar retaining it with a flight of 234 miles. All these flights were completed in about 5 hours and were the result of a combination of thermal upcurrents and great horizontal wind velocity. Previously thermals had not been expected on windy days. Now it was discovered that "wind thermals" offer the best opportunity for long distance soaring.

The 1935 Rhön meet was notable for the great number of long flights; 209 flights covering more than 100 kilometers. This was the result of the government program, favoring the training of a large number of good soaring pilots, rather than a few star performers. Four pilots, Oeltschner, Bräutigam, Heinemann and Steinhoff, established a new distance record of 313 miles, landing at the airport of Brno, Czechoslovakia. On the way back to the Wasserkuppe by airplane tow, Oeltschner was killed in a crash, and to honor their friend the three others requested that the record be listed in his name only.

Motorless flight had now been mastered to the extent that long distances could be covered in motorless planes if the pilot would go wherever favorable currents might bring him. The next step was to learn to reach any point he might choose. Goal flights had been practiced since the first Rhön meetings, but in 1935 for the first time such flights were made over long distances; in this year Peter Riedel made a 165-mile goal flight from Berlin to Hamburg, later Kraft flew 208 miles from Hornberg to Cologne, and during the Olympic games in 1936 the Hungarian, Ludwig Rotter, made a goal flight from Berlin to Kiel.

A further development from the goal flight was the sailplane tour over a predetermined course, which had to be flown within a specified time and with scheduled stops, regardless of terrain and weather conditions. The first tour, covering 432 miles over the route Darmstadt—Würzburg—München—Augsburg—Stuttgart—Mannheim—Darmstadt, was completed in 1936 by four pilots. Another challenge to the skill of soaring pilots was the crossing of the Alps, and this was achieved by six sailplanes, including a two-seater, during the ISTUS meet at Salzburg early in 1937.

Long goal flights soon became a matter of routine. For example, one day during the 1937 Rhön contest twenty pilots listed Nürnberg, almost 100 miles distant, as their goal, and nineteen made it. In 1938 "distance with return to starting point" was added to the record list, the record holder being Bernhard Flinch with a flight from Bremen to Lübeck and back, 191 miles.

The 1938 Rhön meet was remarkable for a great number of high altitude flights. The record was raised to 21,398 feet by Walter Drechsel, and there were no less than forty flights to over 13,000 feet. Many of these were made by flying blind through thunderclouds, a feat which previously had been considered extremely reckless. Before the end of the year the record was raised to 22,560 feet by Erwin Ziller.

In 1937 records for two-seaters were first officially recognized, and soon approached those for single-seaters, in the case of duration even surpassing the single-seater record when in December 1938 A. Bödecker and K. H. Zander remained in the air for 50 hours, 26 minutes.

The motorless flight movement outside Germany had progressed so far that by 1937 other countries could offer serious competition to Germany's best sailplane pilots. This was demonstrated in the great International Soaring Contest at the Wasserkuppe in July, where seven nations took part. Germany won the contest on points, but Poland, Switzerland, Austria and England took prizes although their pilots did not have the advantage the Germans had of being thoroughly familiar with the terrain.

Reports came from Russia of great distance flights. In May 1937 Victor Rastorgueff, flying eastward from Moscow, covered first 335 miles, then 374 miles, and finally on May 27, 405 miles. On the same day V. M. Ilchenko with V. Emerik as passenger established a two-seater record of 253 miles, and this was raised to almost 400 miles by I. Kartasheff and P. Savtzov in July 1938.

On July 6, 1939, a new world's single seater distance record of 465 miles was made by a woman, O. Klepikova.

The number of "Silver C's" awarded indicates the progress of motorless flight in the various countries. In December 1938 Germany, far in the lead, had 816; Poland had 159; Great Britain 50; France 29; Switzerland 19; and the United States 17.

Great Britain twice held the official duration record for two-seaters in 1937 and 1938. A Polish girl, Wanda Modlibowska, established a duration record for women of over 24 hours in 1937.

National soaring contests are now held in many countries, the Elmira meet in the United States having been held annually since 1930. The official American distance record of 212 miles was flown by Lewin B. Barringer on April 19, 1938, from Wichita Falls, Texas, to Tulsa, Oklahoma. It was the first long goal flight in America and was made from winch launching over level country. This was later surpassed by Robert Stanley with a flight of 219 miles, which lacked by 3 miles the necessary 5% over for a new record.

In June 1939 Woodbridge P. Brown established a new American distance and goal record of 263 miles from Wichita Falls, Texas, to Wichita, Kansas. The altitude record was raised to 17,264 feet by Robert Stanley on July 4, 1939.

With the erection of permanent buildings at government expense at the Warren E. Eaton site on Harris Hill at Elmira, gliding and soaring in the United States has begun to come of age. In addition to the Annual National Contest at Elmira there are regional meets in California, Michigan, Texas and New Jersey. With the government actively sponsoring the training of college students as airplane pilots, it is likely that this help will be extended to the motorless field which will furnish the needed impetus to have the sport increase until thousands of young men and women can take advantage of the wonderful soaring conditions that exist all over the United States.

CHAPTER II

AERODYNAMICS

By Paul Schweizer
Assisted by Milton Stoughton and
Ernest Schweizer

GLIDING FLIGHT

WHILE THE AERODYNAMICS of soaring flight may at first glance appear to be somewhat mysterious and complex, in reality the whole thing resolves in the simple "glide." All the art and science of gliding and soaring is built up around this simple phenomenon.

A powerless aircraft is said to be "gliding" when it slides along and down through still air in the same manner that a sled slides down the snowy slope of a hill. While it may at times be sliding on a steeper angle than at others, it is *always* coming *downhill* in this air. Having no power of its own to propel it, there is no other way to maintain forward motion except by letting its own weight pull it ahead just as a sled or a cart moves down a hill. The only difference is that in this case the wings are the "wheels" or "runners," and the air is the "hill" on which it slides. Just how fast it will glide downhill, and how steeply, depends upon the design of the glider and on how the pilot controls it.

The very efficient high performance gliders can glide a long way without losing much height. In fact, some can "coast" 30 miles in still air for every mile of altitude lost, without the help of any rising air currents such as make it possible to keep a glider up for hours at a time. In Fig. 1 is a comparison of the glides of various types of gliders.

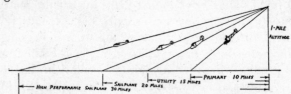

FIG. 1. AVERAGE GLIDES FOR DIFFERENT TYPES OF GLIDERS
IN STILL AIR

Distance from 1-mile altitude

The altitude that a certain glider will lose in a given time is called the "sinking speed" and depends upon the design of the glider and upon how fast the pilot flies it, as the gliding ratio, as it is called, changes with the airspeed. There is always a certain airspeed at which the glider will "sink" the slowest, and another speed, slightly faster, that carries the glider the greatest distance when starting from a given altitude. The slowest rate of descent is called the "minimum sinking speed" and is usually given in feet per second. The sinking speed of a modern high performance sailplane is about 2 feet per second, while as little as 1 foot is possible. Since it is desirable to have a good forward speed and "glide" in order to make long distance flights, gliders are not always designed to have the lowest possible sinking speed. This apparent paradox will be explained in detail later on in the text.

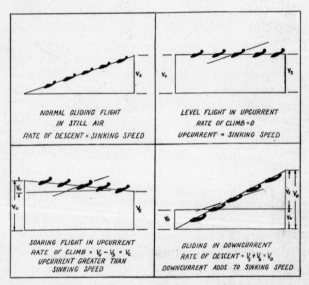

FIG. 2. GLIDING AND SOARING FLIGHT

Soaring flight differs from gliding flight in that the machine flies without losing altitude, and even climbs higher. This is possible because the pilot is flying in a part of the air that is rising bodily, carrying the glider in it, just as a leaf or paper is carried up by the wind. The soaring glider is still sliding downhill in this "body" of air, but not so fast as the whole is rising. So the basic principle of soaring is to get in an upcurrent that is rising more quickly than the glider is going down. The difference between these two will be the resulting climb. In Fig. 2 the various phases of gliding and soaring flight are shown. The art and skill of soaring come in finding and making the most of these rising air currents to gain altitude and fly distances. From this it is evident that the success of a flight depends not only on the performance of the glider but also upon the skill and knowledge of the pilot.

A knowledge of simple and basic aerodynamic principles and formulas will help a great deal to understand the principles of gliding and soaring flight. As figures and equations "frighten" many, the following explanations have been made as simple as possible and yet still contain the actual formulas and equations used in soaring aerodynamics. Of course, for simplification, many of the intermediate steps have not been shown. The average reader can take these for granted and the more advanced readers probably know them.

A glider in flight is supported by the lifting effect of its wings as it passes through the air. This lift is proportional, to some extent, to (a) the size of the wing, (b) the speed that it moves through the air, (c) the weight, or density, of the air, and (d) the particular aerodynamic characteristics of the wing.

It seems logical that the weight or density of the air (the closeness of the air particles) will affect the lift, as the forces on the wing are due to the reaction of these particles on the wing. The greater the density of the air, the more particles can act against the wing with resulting greater force. So it is evident that the lift must be directly proportional to the density.

The lift is also directly proportional to the area, as the amount of wing that can react against the air is proportional to the area. If we have a wing that is twice as large as a given wing in area, it will have twice as much lift.

Unlike the two previous factors, the lift is proportional to the square of the speed, for an increase of speed not only brings a greater amount of air past the wing but also increases the energy that the air particles can give to the wing. For example, if the speed is doubled there is twice as much air passing over the wing at twice the speed, which means that the lift is two "squared" or four times as much.

The lift of the wing is very much dependent upon the shape of the wing, or airfoil section, and also upon the angle of attack, or angle of inclination of the wing against the wind. For simplification this variation of the lift with the angle of attack and shape characteristics (airfoil section) is called the *lift coefficient*. This coefficient also eliminates the question of airspeed when discussing these characteristics.

Putting all these facts into a formula and setting them equal to the lift, we get:

$$\text{Lift} = L = K\ p\ Cl\ S\ V^2$$

where p = density, Cl = lift coefficient, S = area, V = speed and K is a constant to take care of the units of these factors. This lift equation is the basic flight equation.

The same line of reasoning can be used to prove that the drag is dependent upon the same factors, and so we get:

$$\text{Drag} = D = K\ p\ Cdt\ S\ V^2$$

where Cdt is the total drag coefficient for the glider and all the other factors are the same as in the lift equation.

In Fig. 3 is shown a glider in normal gliding flight. The angle

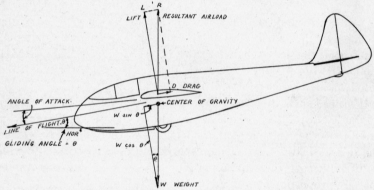

FIG. 3. FORCES ON GLIDER IN FLIGHT

between the line of flight and the horizontal is called the gliding angle θ and the angle that the line of flight makes with the reference chord of the wing is called the angle of attack. Now the lift and drag forces derived above act in gliding flight and are reacted by the weight of the glider. The lift acts perpendicular to the line of flight and the drag parallel to the line of flight. The weight which acts straight down is broken into two parts; w sin θ which is the part that pulls the glider along its path, and w cos θ which is the part of the weight that the lift has to support. R is the resultant air force and it is due to the lift, drag and tail balancing loads, and is equal to W. In a steady glide all these loads balance so that we can set them equal to each other.

$$w \sin \theta = D \qquad\qquad w \cos \theta = L$$

Dividing these by each other we can get them into a very convenient form. $\dfrac{w \sin \theta}{w \cos \theta} = \dfrac{D}{L}$ canceling terms $\dfrac{D}{L} = \dfrac{\sin \theta}{\cos \theta}$

From trigonometry $\dfrac{\sin\theta}{\cos\theta} = \tan\theta$ so $\dfrac{D}{L} = \tan\theta$

Also from previously derived formulas:

$$\frac{D}{L} = \frac{K\ p\ Cdt\ S\ V^2}{K\ p\ Cl\ S\ V^2} = \frac{Cdt}{Cl}$$

Since $\dfrac{D}{L} = \tan\theta$ then $\tan\theta = \dfrac{Cdt}{Cl}$ Or from trig. $\cot\theta = \dfrac{L}{D}$

This shows that the angle of glide depends upon the L/D ratio of the glider and *not* upon the weight of the glider. It is entirely a question of aerodynamic efficiency and does not vary with weight. The L/D ratio is really an efficiency ratio as it shows how much useful lift we can get for a given amount of drag.

Now, referring to Fig. 4, we can get some relation for the sink-

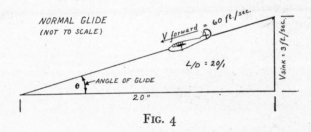

NORMAL GLIDE
(NOT TO SCALE)

V forward = 60 ft./sec.

L/D = 20/1

θ — ANGLE OF GLIDE

20"

Vsink = 3 ft./sec.

FIG. 4

ing speed of the glider. The velocity of the glider along its glide path is Vf and the sinking speed, or velocity downward, is Vs.

By solving this system by trigonometry we get $\sin\theta = \dfrac{Vs}{Vf}$.

However, in the range of gliding angles θ for gliders the sine is substantially equal to the tan.

So we can put $\tan\theta = \dfrac{Vs}{Vf}$, but as $\tan\theta$ also equals $\dfrac{D}{L}$,

we can set $\dfrac{D}{L} = \dfrac{Vs}{Vf}$ or solving for $Vs = \dfrac{Vf}{L/D}$

or putting it in words, the sinking speed is equal to the glider's speed divided by the gliding ratio.

For an example take the glider in Fig. 4. It is traveling along its glide path at 60 ft./sec. and its L/D is 20. From the L/D it is evident that for every 20 feet that the glider moves forward it loses one foot in altitude. So in 1 second it will travel 60 feet or lose 3 feet per second, which is its sinking speed. The same result can be obtained by using the sinking speed formula that we derived and divide the speed (60) by the L/D (20) which will give us 3 ft./sec. sink.

Sinking speed is the basic formula of soaring and until a few years ago the lowest possible sink was the goal of every designer of high performance sailplanes. The plane that had the lowest sink could rise highest on upcurrents and stay up on weak currents that would not enable gliders of greater sinking speed to soar. Today, due to the popularity of cross-country flying, other factors are also important for cross-country gliders.

In order to see upon what sinking speed depends we will put the equation into a different form.

Our original form is $Vs = \dfrac{Vf}{L/D}$

From above $\dfrac{L}{D} = \dfrac{Cl}{Cdt}$ and $L = K\,p\,Cl\,S\,(VS)^2$

As the lift is substantially equal to the weight for usual gliding angles we can substitute the weight for the lift.

So $W = K\,p\,Cl\,(VS)^2$

or solving for $Vf = \sqrt{\dfrac{W}{K\,p\,Cl\,S}} = \sqrt{\dfrac{W}{S}\,\dfrac{1}{K\,p\,Cl}}$

substituting for Vf in $Vs =$

$$\frac{\sqrt{\dfrac{W}{S}\,\dfrac{1}{K\,p\,Cl}}}{Cl/Cdt} = \frac{Cdt}{Cl^{1.5}}\sqrt{\frac{1}{K\,p}}\sqrt{\frac{W}{S}} = \frac{KCdt}{Cl^{1.5}}\sqrt{\frac{W}{S}}$$

From this we see, assuming that the other factors stay the same, that a reduction in weight or an increase in wing area without a corresponding increase in weight will lower the sinking speed. This is evident from the term W/S which is the wing loading (the total weight of the ship divided by the area). Decreasing the weight of the ship is the most obvious method to decrease the sinking speed and was about the only approach used by the early glider pioneers.

Now if the formula is put into another form we will see how the problem of reducing sinking speed was approached from a different angle with much improved results. A new term, *aspect ratio,* now comes into the discussion. This term is really a slenderness ratio of the wing and for a rectangular wing it is equal to the span divided by the chord. However, with curved and tapered wings this ratio is equal to the span ^{2} divided by the area, a more general formula that can be used for any type of wing. From this it is evident that the higher the ratio the more slender the wing.

Changing the form of the aspect ratio equation we get

$A.R. = \dfrac{B^2}{Area}$ $Area = S = \dfrac{B^2}{A.R.}$ where B is the span.

Substituting this in formula No. 1 for sinking speed we get:

$$Vs = \frac{KCdt}{Cl^{1.5}} \sqrt{\frac{W}{\frac{B^2}{AR}}} = \frac{K\,Cd}{Cl^{1.5}} \sqrt{\frac{W}{B^2}} \sqrt{A.R.}$$

In this form, again assuming that the other factors remain unchanged, we see that an increase in span will decrease the sinking speed considerably as it is to the first power while the wing loading of the previous form was to the half power. The term W/B^2 is called the span loading and is equal to the weight divided by the span squared. A low span loading is a good indication of low sinking speed and, as will be explained later, it is more important than aspect ratio for minimum sinking speed, although one is dependent upon the other.

The early designers had carried lightness to the extreme, following along the first line of reasoning, and any further development along this line did not yield much improvement but seriously endangered the strength of the gliders. Following the second line of reasoning increase of span resulted in much improved sinking speeds. This also brought improvements in gliding angles and speed characteristics which spurred development.

The previous discussion has taken place under the assumption that the drag and lift coefficients stayed the same while the other factors varied. Actually these coefficients vary greatly with design, and also with span and aspect ratio. In fact improving the lift and drag characteristics is highly important in lowering the sinking speed and general performance. The following discussion will show what factors determine these lift and drag coefficients.

The lift and drag coefficients as they appear in the previous two formulas are for the complete ship. As the other parts of the glider contribute very little, if any, to the lift, the lift coefficient is just for the wing. The drag coefficient is composed of the drag of the wing and also the other various drags of the glider. The lift coefficient will be discussed first.

As mentioned before the lift is very much dependent upon the wing shape and airfoil section. The first airplanes had flat surfaces for wings which derived lift from the air stream hitting their inclined surface, much as a kite flies. However, it was soon discovered that by curving the wing and giving it two surfaces, top and bottom, the lift could be greatly improved and in present-day airfoils most of the lift is due to the action of the top surface of the wing and only a small part to the effect of the air stream hitting the bottom surface.

By varying the shape of the airfoil section, the characteristics can be radically changed. There are thousands of different airfoil shapes available, each with its special features. The designer chooses the one that suits his purpose best or else designs one of his own. In Fig. 5 a set of curves is plotted in the conventional manner for an airfoil. The lift and drag coefficients, L/D and center of pressure are plotted against the angle of attack or speed as each angle is proportional to a different speed. As the angle of attack increases

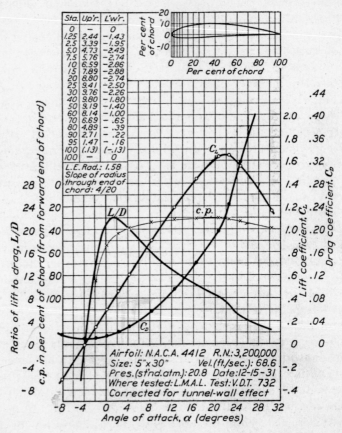

FIG. 5

the speed decreases and the lift coefficient increases. This is evident from the formula for lift, $L = K p Cl S V^2$. For a given plane in level flight the only variables are lift and speed, as the wing area, density and constant are fixed at any altitude. So if one of these factors is increased the other must decrease in order to balance.

As the lift coefficient increases with angle of attack there is a point where the curve suddenly changes direction and the lift goes down. This is known as the stall. Here the airflow around the wing suddenly changes form and the lift is very much decreased. In flight this sudden loss of lift causes the ship to drop. Some airfoils will cause the ship to drop relatively slowly, or "mush," while others will lose most of their lift and drop the ship much faster. As a rule when stalled the nose of the ship drops and with the loss of some altitude it will pick up speed and lift again. The main danger of the stall lies in the fact that most gliders and airplanes will start to autorotate or "spin" in the stalled position if some gust or unbalanced weight or force should cause the plane to start turning. So it is important that the plane is in rig; that is, so balanced that it wants to keep in a level position and not turn off to one side or drop a wing. However, by special design and/or by the use of special devices, a plane can be prevented from stalling and hence eliminate the spin.

In using the airfoil curves in Fig. 5, it is important that the scale effect be considered. As these curves are determined experimentally in the wind tunnel with small models under different speeds, pressures and other conditions, it is important that the results be corrected to the conditions of the glider. In order to facilitate this, a factor called the *Reynold's Number* (R.N.) is used to correct for this, and it is dependent upon the speed, size and density of the air. Knowing the size of the glider and conditions of operation, the R.N. can be determined from the formula R.N. $= 6350$ v l where v is the speed in ft./sec., l is the wing chord in feet, and 6350 is the constant for standard air. Knowing the R.N. of the glider, one can then get data at this number or correct to this condition.

Of all the wing characteristics, the maximum lift is about the most susceptible to scale effect. As a rule one never gets the maximum lift as given in the usual Cl curves. This means that the stalling and landing speed are higher than would be expected. The shape of the peak of the lift curve and the type of stall are also closely tied in with scale effect and vary considerably for large variations in R.N. Other factors such as drag, moment coefficient, center of pressure, etc., do not show so much change. It might be mentioned here that the maximum lift and type of stall depend also upon the wing plan form, surface smoothness, interference and other factors.

In choosing an airfoil for a glider there are many features that enter into the choice, such as: the L/D, maximum lift, minimum drag, moment (twisting) coefficient, allowable depth for spars, scale effect, ease of construction, etc. Of course the design and purpose of the glider determine which of these factors are most important. However, the most obvious indication of a good airfoil is its efficiency ratio or L/D ratio. The L/D listed in the airfoil reports is only for the wing and does not include the drag and lift of the other parts of the ship. These parts add little, if any, to the lift of the ship but add considerably to the drag. This causes the L/D ratio to drop considerably.

The airfoil data given are usually for a wing of aspect ratio of 6 and so must be corrected to the aspect ratio of the glider. If it is over 6 then there will be a decrease in the drag due to the decrease in drag with increase in aspect ratio. But this is a problem in drag and will be explained below.

The total drag coefficient is divided basically into what is called the "parasite" drag (it does not result from a directly useful function) and the "induced" drag which results directly from the lifting force on the glider. The parasite drag is made up of the "profile" drag of the wing and the form drag of the fuselage, tail, and any other projecting or exposed items that cause a disturbance of the airflow. This drag also includes the interference between fuselage and wing, wings and struts, etc. It does not include the effect of the presence of the fuselage on the flow over the wings, which can alter the induced drag due to the lift, by changing the distribution of loading over the wings.

While the profile drag coefficient of the wing is entirely a matter of the sectional shape of the wing section and secondarily of size (scale effect) and attitude, induced drag is a matter of the wing shape in plan and of the load distribution over the wing span. The drag results directly from deflecting the air downward behind the wing to provide lift. At slow speeds the air must be deflected down more sharply than at high speeds, so the induced drag coefficient is high at high angles of attack of the wing (low speeds) and low at the low angles of attack (high speeds). Thus at high speeds in a powerplane the induced drag is almost negligible. However, in glider design, especially for those not designed for high speed cross-country work, the induced drag is never negligible in the normal operating speed range.

This will be clearer if we study the formula for the induced drag coefficient. The induced drag coefficient $= Cl^2/\pi AR$ where Cl is the lift coefficient of the wing and AR is the aspect ratio of the wing. This shows how it is most important at high lift coefficients and that it is decreased with larger aspect ratios. As the lift is substantially fixed the induced drag is lessened by increasing the aspect ratio. This is one reason for the comparatively large span of sailplanes.

Since the weight of the wings runs up rapidly with increasing aspect ratios, and the maneuverability is reduced, a compromise is usually established between these conflicting factors. The best design is the one resulting from the wisest choice of compromises: but perfection is unattainable as requirements and results are still a matter of opinion.

In general, the effect of high aspect ratio is to reduce the induced drag. The elliptical wing shape is the theoretical ideal, but it can be approximated closely by wings with a straight center section and tapered tips. The straight wing and the too sharply tapered wing are not so efficient as the elliptical or properly tapered wing. A poorly located or improperly faired fuselage can alter the distribution of air loading over the wings and have the effect of increasing the induced drag. It is also possible for the fuselage interference to decrease the induced drag by offsetting the effect of a too sharply tapered wing.

The fuselage and tail surfaces are the remaining important parts causing the parasite drag of a glider. A well shaped fuselage may have scarcely more drag than the tail surfaces. Its drag consists of a combination of the effect of the surface area (skin friction) and the form or shape of the fuselage. If the shape is very good, the total drag approaches that of pure skin friction. This latter value varies with the scale effect and the quality of surface finish. In this respect it behaves similarly to the profile drag of the wing.

At high speeds especially, the smoothness of a surface is an important factor in performance. This is true particularly on aircraft of high speed design where small items can loom large in power losses. In gliders, of course, although it is not so important, these losses appear as reduced gliding range and increased sinking speed.

With respect to the shape that produces the least drag in a streamlined body or strut, it is interesting to note that it is the forward portion that is the most sensitive to variations in shape or to small interferences which cause local turbulence. For this reason great care should always be exercised to obtain the least possible disturbance of the natural lines of a fuselage when designing windshields or closed cabins. The intersection between the wing and the fuselage is also of primary importance, since improper arrangement here will also cause unnecessary drag and interference with the wing lift distribution. Fillets between the wing and fuselage intersection are usually necessary for low wing positions to avoid drag and stalling difficulties. On mid-wing and higher locations the problem is not so difficult. In many cases the best solution is no fillets at all.

A well shaped fuselage section is more or less rounded so that there are no very sharp corners to cause drag when the air is flowing at an angle to it, and whose longitudinal shape is approximately an ellipse forward of the maximum section and a parabola aft to the tail. The shape of a symmetrical airfoil section expanded to the desired depth also makes a good fuselage form. In general, the exact shape of the basic form is far less important than the nature of the disturbances and interferences caused by the addition of wires, cockpit enclosures, etc., since these usually have a powerful effect on the character of the airflow over the combination of parts.

This principle also applies to wings where it is more important to hold the contour of the nose of the airfoil so that there is no break in the true curve over the spar, where the fabric is usually attached, and to provide a highly finished surface, than it is to use the most efficient airfoil section. The theoretical gains are small in comparison to the gains that can be obtained with a little care and high grade workmanship. The avoidance of round struts or wires, very oblique struts, venturis, and other "drag producers" will help to increase the performance.

STABILITY

A glider can fly steadily on a straight path because of its "balance" and "stability." Both conditions are obtained by means of the tail surfaces or by special design of the wing to get the same effect on a tailless glider. Since the air forces on the wing are not the same at all angles of attack but shift fore and aft, and the center of gravity is fixed, the glider is balanced at any desired angle of attack by means of the tail surface "elevator." By tilting the elevator, the load on the tail is varied to obtain any desired angle of attack, which in turn fixes the airspeed. Thus, at low angles of attack (low lift), the airspeed becomes higher to sustain the weight and at high angles of attack (high lift) the airspeed is lower. A rigidly fixed tail surface will balance the craft at only one angle of attack and airspeed providing the weight is not changed nor the location of the center of gravity altered. This characteristic can be noted in flying models.

However, a glider might balance but still be unable to make a steady flight for the lack of sufficient stability. After being disturbed in flight the ship should right itself and fly steadily without too many oscillations. The fixed portion of the horizontal tail surfaces is called the stabilizer and its purpose is to keep the glider from diving or stalling. It must have sufficient area and the distance that it is placed back from the center of gravity with respect to the wing is also of importance in obtaining longitudinal stability (stability up or down along its flight path).

The stability necessary to keep the aircraft from turning off its straightaway course is furnished by the fixed part of the vertical tail surfaces called the *fin*. This is the same as the weathercock effect on the familiar weathervane. The rudder on the vertical surface acts the same as the fin whenever it is held stationary by the rudder control.

To keep the glider from rolling off sidewise into a "sideslip," dihedral angle is supplied to the wings. The wing has dihedral angle when the tips are higher than the center of the wing. This may be a very small and almost negligible angle in some cases, but the present trend is toward more dihedral to give better stability in circling.

In general the more stable an aircraft is, the slower and more difficult it is to maneuver. Consequently experience has taught what minimum amount of stability is satisfactory for various types of airplanes and gliders, without introducing other disadvantages. Training gliders emphasize stability while aerobatic sailplanes feature maneuverability. Special care is necessary to avoid obtaining "spiral instability" by having too much directional stability compared to lateral stability. This results in a condition where the plane tends to tighten itself into a sharp spiral flight unless it is held out of it by the aileron control, when making a normal turn. The opposite condition of too much lateral stability relative to directional stability results in a sort of wallowing motion commonly known as the "Dutch Roll." This combination is not so common as the other, however. If a rudder and fin is made large enough to provide the needed directional control, there will usually be plenty of directional stability. Sufficient dihedral angle is then provided on the wing to avoid spiral instability.

Lateral stability also depends upon the characteristics of the wing design besides the dihedral angle, particularly around the stall. On ordinary tapered wings the tips stall first and as the stall moves in along the span the ailerons become ineffective in this stalled region. Some dissimilarity of the wing or a gust will cause one wing to drop or "fall off," and as the ailerons are ineffective, the glider may drop into a spiral dive or spin.

This can be avoided by using "aerodynamic" twist, which is the change of section along the span so that the tips will stall later than the center part of the wing. This can be done more easily, but not quite so efficiently, by using "geometric twist," which is the actual twisting of the wing so that the tip is working at a smaller angle of attack than the center and hence stalls later. The second method is the most practical and is called "washing out" the wing. In training gliders it is desirable to have the wings "washed out" and if it is not built into the wing some provision is usually made to adjust it.

The twisting of the wing definitely helps aileron control over the whole flight range as the ailerons are always operating at lower lift. Twist may also improve performance slightly by decreasing the induced drag. This is due to the possibility of getting elliptical lift distribution from a rectangular wing for *one* angle of attack, by using the proper twist. The general effect is to reduce the lift at the tips which reduces the induced drag.

PERFORMANCE

Fig. 6 shows the general performance curves at sea level of a clean intermediate class sailplane. The curves plotted are the L/D and the sinking speed against the airspeed. These curves are typical, with a rapid increase of L/D and sinking speeds at the higher values of forward speeds. It is interesting to note on the sinking speed curve that the best forward speed to fly for minimum descent is approximately 5 m.p.h. above the stall. This figure holds in general for most gliders and shows the fallacy of flying the ship near the stall for minimum sinking speed.

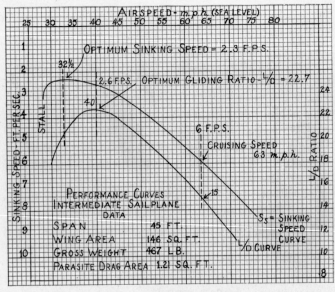

Fig. 6

The speed for flattest glide is about 7 m.p.h., in this case, above the minimum sinking speed. In very efficient sailplanes this spread would be much greater. The best general "soaring" speed is usually taken as being half-way between the minimum sinking speed and the maximum gliding ratio. For this model it is just about 36 m.p.h. The cruising speed is the speed at which the sinking speed is 6 ft./sec. This has been arbitrarily set at this value and it is just a means of comparing the high speed qualities of sailplanes. The better cross-country ships will have a higher speed for the given 6 ft./sec. sinking speed.

The curves in Fig. 6 are for sea-level operation and are substantially correct for normal soaring heights. At higher altitudes the actual sinking speed and flying speed will be higher, but the value of the gliding ratio is unchanged, it being a function of the design of the glider and angle of attack of the wing.

SAMPLE PERFORMANCE CALCULATIONS

$$\frac{L}{D} = \frac{C_L}{C_D \text{ Total}} = \frac{C_L}{C_{D\text{profile}} + C_{D\text{parasite}} + C_{D\text{Induced}}}$$

$$V_{F.P.S.} = \sqrt{\frac{2W}{Sp\ C_L}} = \sqrt{\frac{2W}{Sp}} \times \frac{1}{\sqrt{C_L}}$$

$$\text{Sinking Speed} = \frac{V_{F.P.S.}}{L/D} \qquad A.R = \frac{b^2}{s} = \frac{(45)^2}{146} = 13.9$$

$$\text{Parasite Drag Area} = 1.21 \text{ sq. ft.} \qquad C_{D\text{parasite}} = \frac{1.21 \times 1.25}{146} = .01035$$

$$\frac{W}{S} = \frac{467}{146} = 3.2 \qquad p = .002378$$

$$V_{F.P.S.} = \sqrt{\frac{2 \times 467}{146 \times .002378}} \times \frac{1}{\sqrt{C_L}} = \frac{51.9}{\sqrt{C_L}}$$

$$C_{D\text{ induced}} = \frac{C^2_L}{\pi\ (A.R.)} \qquad \begin{array}{c}\text{Correction for}\\ \text{Plan Form} = 1.05\end{array} \qquad C_{D\text{ ind}} = \frac{C^2_L \times 1.05}{\pi\ (AR)}$$

C_L (1)	$C_{D\text{prof.}}$ Corrected (2)	$C_{D\text{ind}}$ (3)	$C_{D\text{tot.}}$ (2) + (3) + $C_{D\text{par}}$ (4)	L/D $\frac{(1)}{(4)}$ (5)	$V_{F.P.S.}$ $\frac{51.9}{\sqrt{C_L}}$ (6)	Sinking Speed $\frac{(6)}{(5)}$ (7)	$V_{M.P.H.}$ $\frac{6}{1.47}$ (8)
.1							
.2							
.3							
.4	.088	.00385	.023	17.38	82.1	4.73	55.8

FIG. 7

This also means that each "indicated" airspeed on the dial of the instrument corresponds to a certain angle of attack of the wing and that the glider will always stall at the same point on the dial. It can be shown also that the best speeds to fly for the minimum sink and the maximum gliding ratio will be at the same "indicated" airspeed on the dial.

The means of determining the performance of gliders and sailplanes is not difficult and the general method will be explained. In Fig. 7 appear the formulas and sample calculations for the same ships as in Fig. 6. The formulas used are those that we have already developed. It is important to note that Cd total equals the sum of the profile, parasite and induced drag coefficient.

It is evident from this that the calculations for speed are definite and accurate except at high angles of attack where the question of stall comes in. This is not important, however, as the performance around this speed is not desired.

The big question in performance calculations is the evaluating of the drag coefficients. The Cd profile must be corrected for the effects of R.N. This may be appreciable and it is best if one has data at the R.N. of the glider. In general the surface of the actual glider wing will not be as smooth as that of the model, necessitating an increase in profile drag, to be estimated by the designer from such data as he can obtain. The induced drag as given by the general formula is for the ideal elliptical wing and must be corrected for all other plan forms. The elliptic wing has the minimum possible induced drag and all others have an increasing amount depending upon how far they vary from the true ellipse. By applying a correction factor we can get an "effective" aspect ratio which is somewhat lower than the actual of the wing and so results in greater induced drag. The value of these corrections varies with plan form. For a rectangular wing it may be from 6-10% for aspect ratios of 5 to 12. For tapered wings which closely approximate the ellipse it will be less than half this amount. Data are available in aerodynamics texts and NACA reports enabling the designer to make a reasonable estimate.

The parasite drag is the most difficult to determine exactly because of its complexity. It consists of the drag of the fuselage, tail surfaces, and bracing, and the effect of interference between parts. The drag of the tail surfaces may include induced drag also besides the profile drag, as the lift on the tail surfaces necessary to balance the ship causes induced drag.

In a sailplane with full cantilever wings and tail surfaces, and no serious external protuberances such as control horns, fittings, open cockpits, etc., the problem of parasite drag becomes relatively easy. It is then just the addition of the fuselage drag and tail surface drag plus the interference drag between fuselage and wing and fuselage and tail surfaces. All these can be determined readily.

In a glider of much lower performance the many struts, wires, open cockpits, exposed fittings, etc., all make the estimate of drag coefficients more difficult. However, in such ships approximate performance figures will suffice. At present very little data is available on sailplane fuselages, but the drags can be estimated from data on similar shapes in various references. It is convenient to compare parasite drags of gliders and other aircraft by expressing it in terms of flat plate area or drag area. The drag area is the area of a flat plate which has the same drag as the ship in question. The drag coefficient of a flat plate is approximately 1.25 per sq. ft. The performance curves given as an example are based upon a flat plate area of 1.21 sq. ft. It is usually convenient to express this in terms of wing area and so the coefficient obtained by multiplying the area by the drag coefficient is divided by the wing area. This puts the coefficients in the same units as the other drag coefficients of the wing and it can be added directly.

The calculations are worked out for Cl equals .4. The Cd profile at this Cl is taken from the airfoil curves and corrected for scale effect if necessary. The Cd induced is determined from the regular induced drag formula multiplied by a factor of 1.05 to correct for plan form. The parasite determined above is added to these two, giving the total drag of the ship. The L/D is determined by dividing the lift coefficient by this total drag coefficient. From the standard flight equation the speed for Cl equals .4 is determined. Dividing this speed by the L/D will give the sinking speed in ft./sec. This is worked out for each Cl and the results are plotted as in Fig. 6.

The high performance of the modern sailplane results mainly from the reduction of drag. This is accomplished by designing the fuselage as "clean" and small as possible with all unnecessary protuberances eliminated, and selecting the most suitable wing section, plan form, span, aspect ratio, etc. It becomes very important to reduce the induced drag in order to get high performance. This is accomplished by using a comparatively large wing span, giving a low value of "span loading," which is the key to a low induced drag. This also results in a high aspect ratio, but it is the span loading rather than the aspect ratio which reduces the drag.

Fig. 8 is the "polar" drag curve of the glider whose performance is given in Fig. 6, with the actual drag in pounds plotted against airspeed. The drag is divided into its usual three parts; induced, profile and parasite. This shows how the drag is divided and how it varies with the speed. The induced drag decreases as the speed goes up because it is dependent upon the lift coefficient, so that at

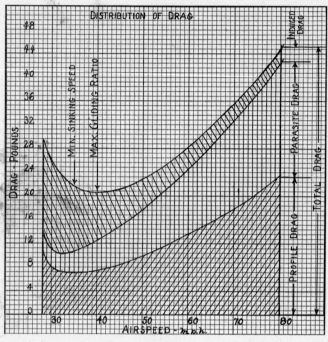

FIG. 8

high speeds the induced drag is only a very small per cent of the total drag. The profile and the parasite drag, however, increase with speed.

It is interesting to note that the performance of a given glider can be improved at speeds above optimum by increasing the wing loading. This has the effect of moving the L/D curve in Fig. 6 horizontally to the right. Thus if the glider in the example were loaded so as to move the L/D curve 5 miles to the right, at 60 m.p.h. the ratio would be increased from 16.2 to 18.2, and the sinking speed would be reduced from 5.4 f.p.s. to 4.8 f.p.s., or a reduction of .6 f.p.s. This sort of overloading is useful only on long fast flights, and cannot be done unless there is a margin of strength in the structure to carry the overload safely.

CHAPTER III

TYPES OF GLIDERS

By Lewin B. Barringer

IN THE EARLY DEVELOPMENT of motorless, heavier-than-air aircraft there were a number of different glider types. The first successful type was the hang glider, so named because in flight the pilot hung from his armpits or elbows. There were no movable control surfaces on these primitive types, which could only be balanced statically by the pilot shifting his weight by moving his legs. The first successful hang glider built by Lilienthal was a monoplane, but he later also developed a biplane type. Octave Chanute experimented with multi-wing designs including one with five superimposed planes. His greatest success, however, was with the biplane type later brought to a higher degree of development by the Wright brothers who built movable wings and tail surfaces for control and lay on the lower wing instead of hanging through it.

Another type of hang glider was the tandem built by Montgomery in California. This design had two planes mounted one behind the other with the pilot hanging between them from the framework by which they were attached. It is interesting to note that a contemporary Californian has built a biplane hang glider to experience the thrill of taking off after self launching by running down a hill. This glider has conventional control surfaces actuated by a small control stick. Landing is made on a single wheel and tail skid. Its use is limited to short gliding flights.

Although the most successful early types were biplanes, all modern gliders are now monoplanes divided into four types: the primary glider, the secondary or utility glider, the intermediate sailplane, and the high performance sailplane. The term sailplane is generally used to denote a glider with performance capable of real soaring flights such as the requirements of the "Silver C" license. There are no sharp dividing lines between these types, but their general characteristics are distinct enough for the accepted classifications.

THE PRIMARY GLIDER

The primary glider is the lightest, least expensive and simplest in construction of the glider types. It has a high monoplane wing and tail surfaces braced by wires or struts and an open truss-braced fuselage. The pilot's seat is entirely open and unprotected.

The span of the square, untapered wing of the average primary is about 34 feet with an aspect ratio of 7 to 1. Its weight empty is about 175 pounds. With a wing area of 170 square feet the wing loading in flight is under 2 pounds per square foot. The gliding ratio is about 12 to 1 with a sinking speed of 4 feet per second. Stalling speed is 20-23 m.p.h.

Philip Ellicott Barringer

A WACO PRIMARY GLIDER (1930-1931)

The fuselage construction of the average primary is entirely of wood with the exception of the metal fittings. Several makes have been built, however, with fuselages of brazed or welded light steel tubing which are capable of standing up somewhat better under prolonged abuse of student training. Wing construction is of wood, fabric-covered, employing two spars. Drag loads within the wing are taken by cross-bracing of wire or wood.

The use of the primary glider should be restricted to airport gliding and instruction through the "B" license stage of making 360° turns from heights up to 400 feet. Although successful soaring flights have been made with primaries, they should not be used for this type of flying as they lack sufficient strength, stability and control for adequate safety in the turbulent air conditions sometimes found in slope soaring. There is no protection for the pilot in case of a crash.

The cost of a new primary glider is about $385. It also can be purchased in kit form for home assembly at a price around $185. A few good used primaries are sometimes available at prices of $100 upwards.

THE SECONDARY GLIDER

The secondary, or utility glider, as the American version is generally called, is more refined than the primary in that it has an enclosed fuselage, a more efficient wing braced by streamline struts and a pneumatic landing wheel equipped with a brake. This type is rapidly gaining favor over the primary for training despite its higher cost. The reasons for this are its superior advantages with respect to pilot protection, ruggedness, control and performance. For most clubs the last mentioned consideration is probably the deciding one as the utility type can be used for both primary training and soaring. It is ideal for slope soaring and can also be used for thermal soaring, although its slow forward speed and lack of maneuverability as compared to a sailplane make it rather inefficient for this advanced flying.

The utility usually has a rectangular wing with rounded tips, a span of about 36 feet and an aspect ratio of 8. Its weight empty is about 220 pounds which, with a disposable load of 200 pounds for the pilot, parachute and instruments and a wing area of 180 square feet, gives a wing loading of from 2.5 to 2.8 pounds per square foot. The gliding ratio is about 15 to 1 with a sinking speed of 3½ feet per second. Stalling speed is 24-26 m.p.h.

Hans Groenhoff

STEVENS-FRANKLIN UTILITY GLIDER

An interesting conversion of a utility glider is the Stevens-Franklin. Tapered, gull wings of 48 feet span with the same wing area as a standard Franklin utility were developed by a group of engineering students at the Stevens Institute of Technology to fit on the Franklin fuselage and use the same struts. The increase in control and performance is very marked, the gliding ratio being about 17 to 1 and the sinking speed under 3 feet per second, bringing this glider almost into the intermediate sailplane class.

The cost of a utility glider is about $600 new, including a trailer for transporting it disassembled. Some firms have put out partly-assembled kits for a price of about half this amount. Used secondaries or utilities in good condition and with trailers can sometimes be purchased for $350 upwards.

THE INTERMEDIATE SAILPLANE

The intermediate or training sailplane is a somewhat recent development to fill the gap between the secondary glider and the high performance sailplane. Due to its exceedingly low aerodynamic drag and its very flat gliding angle the latter type is often difficult to fly for the student trained in the former. The intermediate sailplane fills this gap perfectly so that the transition is more gradual and consequently safer.

The chief differences between this type and the secondary are its greater span with higher aspect ratio, higher cruising speed and generally cleaner design. The span of the average intermediate sailplane is 45-48 feet and the aspect ratio 14. Built to stand the stresses of soaring in rough air and aerobatics, its weight is about 290 pounds and wing area 170 square feet, giving a wing loading in flight of about 3 pounds per square foot.

The first reaction of a student after flying an intermediate sailplane is its "slippery" feel due to its clean design and resultant low drag. Its gliding ratio is about 20 to 1 and sinking speed about 2.8 feet per second. Stalling speed is 26-30 m.p.h.

Cost of an intermediate sailplane when new is about $750. This is the price of the Bowlus "Baby Albatross" which can also be purchased in kit form for $425 available in separate units, the first costing $75 and each subsequent unit $35. An excellent American intermediate is the ABC Sailplane, designed and built by Arthur B. Schultz, President of the Detroit Glider Council. It won the Eaton Design Competition for the most practical American glider produced in 1937. A set of detail working plans for this sailplane are available at a cost of $35. There are still so few intermediate sailplanes that used ones are seldom on the market.

HIGH PERFORMANCE SAILPLANE

The most advanced type of sailplane, usually designated as high performance, is the most beautiful and perhaps also the most efficient of all heavier-than-air aircraft. This type a few years ago was char-

Frank Turgeon, Jr.

THE BOWLUS - DU PONT "ALBATROSS" HIGH PERFORMANCE
SAILPLANE OF 1934

GÖPPINGEN I "WOLF"
INTERMEDIATE
SAILPLANE

Hans Groenhoff

THE ROSS "IBIS" HIGH PERFORMANCE SAILPLANE TAKING OFF

Hans Groenhoff

acterized by large wing spans of more than 60 feet. An example was the Bowlus-du Pont "Albatross" which measured 62 feet from tip to tip of its highly tapered wings. This sailplane was typical of the best designs at that time, none of which were quite so clean or nearly so strong as modern high performance sailplanes. Although an extreme limit of 98 feet span was reached in the "Austria," spans have now come down in the interest of greater maneuverability necessary for efficient spiraling in thermal upcurrents and ease of handling on the ground. They vary from the 48 feet of the American Ross "Ibis" to 50 and 56 respectively for the German "Rhönsperber" and "Minimoa" designs. Aspect ratios average about 16 to 1, although some experimental German designs have been as great as 30 to 1. Weight of these sailplanes will vary from the 310 pounds of the small Ross to 520 pounds for the 1937 model of the "Minimoa." Wing areas vary from 125 to 205 square feet for the two types. Wing loadings are from 3½ to 4 pounds per square foot.

The most outstanding of the flying characteristics of the high performance type is its extraordinarily flat gliding ratio. The Ross and "Minimoa" are both about 26 to 1. Experimental German types have gone as high as 33 to 1. This flat glide coupled with a low sinking speed of 2 feet per second naturally gives this sailplane excellent climbing ability. At a soaring contest where a number of gliders of different types are slope soaring the high performance sailplanes soon climb 500 or 1000 feet higher than the secondaries.

Other important flying characteristics of this type are its cruising speed of about 40 m.p.h. which is 2 to 5 miles above the stalling speed, and its efficient speed range. The best of these sailplanes have a sinking speed of just under 2 feet per second at the cruising speed of 40 m.p.h. The clean design helps it to fly quickly through the downdrafts without much loss of altitude.

On the author's distance record flight with a "Minimoa" the 212 miles were covered at an average speed, measured for the airline distance, of 37 m.p.h. There was an average tail wind of about 25 m.p.h., but when there is also taken into consideration the facts that the actual course covered was at least 260 miles and that during the greater percentage of the time the sailplane was being spiraled, its speed performance becomes more apparent. The world distance record of 405 miles was made in 8¼ hours, an average of close to 50 m.p.h.

In keeping with the general streamlining of this type, the pilot's cockpit is entirely enclosed. As well as helping the streamlining it also often is a necessity for pilot protection from airflow at high speeds or from cold at high altitudes. On a flight made in the "Ibis" in New Hampshire the temperature was 12° F. at 9500 feet altitude, but due to the fact that the ship was soaring in the sunlight above the clouds the inside cockpit temperature was a comfortable 75° F. On the world record altitude flight to over 26,000 feet above sea level a temperature of 40° below zero F. was experienced.

Hans Groenhoff

THE SCHWEIZER TWO-PLACE, ALL METAL, HIGH PERFORMANCE SAILPLANE

Due to its size and complexity of design and construction the high performance sailplane is the most expensive of gliders. Average prices usually vary from $1200 to $2500.

Several two-seater sailplanes have been built, falling in the last three categories. Their performances are the best criterion of the proper classification. An outstanding sailplane of this type is the all-metal Schweizer sailplane which combines high performance with the ease of handling of a utility. Specifications of this ship, with which a national altitude record was made, are as follows: span, 52 ft.; aspect ratio, 12.6; weight empty, 450 lb.; wing area, 214 sq. ft.; gliding ratio, 23.5. Its price is $1300.

CHAPTER IV

DESIGN, CONSTRUCTION AND MAINTENANCE

By Paul and Ernest Schweizer

THIS DISCUSSION OF glider and sailplane design and construction is not intended to be a text on the subject. Glider design is essentially a branch of aeronautical engineering and requires technical knowledge, as well as knowledge of gliding, on the part of the designer. Many gliders have been built without any formal technical knowledge by men who learned from practical experience and by cut-and-try methods. This type of work has enabled many to fly gliders but on the other hand many others were discouraged because of the poor results obtained and the accidents which happened rather frequently. Persons with limited technical knowledge who wish to design and build gliders should at least have the advice and supervision of someone with this necessary knowledge. Lack of supervision in building and operating gliders brought on the rigid regulations now in force. It is much more satisfactory for all concerned that a good set of plans be followed exactly. This discussion is intended to cover the various types of construction, to give general comparisons and to point out the problems the designer must consider and work out in his designs.

LOADS AND STRESSES ON STRUCTURE

The strength and design requirements for gliders and sailplanes are set by the Civil Aeronautics Authority of the federal government and they are based upon past experience and research in this country and abroad. It is obvious that the different types of gliders and sailplanes require different strengths. The strength factors used for training gliders and sailplanes are much different from those used for cloud flying or aerobatic sailplanes. To take care of these different factors, the requirements are based upon flight, gust, and towing speeds instead of having special requirements for each particular type. This method allows the designer to pick his speeds to suit the purpose of his ship more closely. The glider is then placarded with these speeds as limiting speeds which should not be exceeded.

The strength and design requirements represent the minimum strength, etc., necessary for safe operation under given conditions. It is obviously impossible and certainly impractical to design for all possible conditions in which gliders and sailplanes might fly. Nature is capable of an infinite variety of releases of atmospheric energy in which an aircraft may find itself. It is up to the pilot's experience and discretion, and quite often up to chance, to avoid conditions that exceed the strength limits of his plane. Safety factors and extra design margins take care of many unusual conditions but it is impossible to take care of all.

There are three types of loads that act on gliders and sailplanes in flight: gust loads, maneuvering loads, and towing loads. Gust loads are due to sudden changes of speed or direction of the air in which the plane is flying. Maneuvering loads are caused by controlling the plane in flight. Towing loads occur in winch, automobile or airplane towed flight. These three types of loads may act separately or in a variety of combinations.

It is quite apparent that sailplanes in search of upcurrents will encounter gusts, as an upcurrent is essentially a gust of rising air. These sudden accelerations, possible in all directions, build up loads in the structure of the plane entering them proportional to the gust speed, the flight speed, and the sharpness of the gust. The strength of gusts to be expected for different conditions has been determined from experience and checked by flying through them with recording instruments. Through logical formulas, the strength required to resist these gusts can be determined for any speed of gust and flight. In most cases it is the gust loads that determine the designs of the wing and the supporting structure.

In normal gliding and soaring, the maneuvering loads are considerably less than the gust loads. The loads in sharply-banked turns or in an occasional sharp pull-up are about the maximum maneuvering loads normally experienced. In cloud and storm flying the maneuvering loads may be high because of the necessity of adequate control in rough air at high speeds. But here again the gust condition is the design condition as the gusts in storm clouds are extremely strong and sharp edged. Gliders designed for stunting and unlimited aerobatics will almost always be designed by the maneuvering loads. It is evident that severe strains can be put on a ship in this type of flying.

Towing loads are determined to a large degree by the method of towing used. Airplane towing imposes the smallest loads of any of the various methods. In the average towing condition the load on the towline is approximately the drag of the sailplane. The danger in airplane towing does not lie in the actual towing loads or forces but in the speed at which the glider is being towed. If it hits a gust at this speed the loads on the glider are naturally greater than at normal gliding speeds. Also if any sharp maneuvers are made while in tow the loads will quickly build up.

In auto and winch towing the loads are large for ordinary conditions and can easily become excessive in windy and gusty weather. The wings of the glider support not only the weight of the glider, but also the load on the towrope and the balancing load on the tail. The intensity of load on the towrope has actually been measured in flight and during a tow of a utility was found to be as high as 500 pounds. Apparently it often goes above this as towropes of greater strength frequently break in towing. It is the practice to limit the loads on the towrope by putting a weak link in the line. This will allow the rope to break before excessive loads can be put on the ship. In most cases the gust condition will cover towing conditions but the towing speeds should be limited to keep within this range. The nose of the fuselage has to be designed to carry the rope loads which may sometimes act almost vertically.

Shock-cord launching, although not imposing great loads on the wings, does require adequate strength in the fuselage. As the shock-cord loads may easily go over 1000 pounds, it can readily be seen that the fuselage between the nose-hook and hold-back point has to be quite strong. This load more than takes care of the tension loads (forward) of the other types of towing.

As these various types of flight loads can occur separately or in various combinations, their combined effects also must be investigated. Towing in gusty weather with excessive maneuvers necessary to keep the ship in line represents a combination of all three that can very easily be encountered. Although it is poor practice to fly in very gusty weather these conditions do occur and should be considered in design.

All loads considered so far have been flight loads. Although these are of primary importance they are not the only design conditions. Landing, handling, and crash loads have to be considered also if a practical ship is to result.

Handling loads play an important part in the design of gliders and sailplanes, because of the general lightness of construction. In many places the strength required to meet the air loads is not sufficient to take care of the handling loads. The wing tips, although taking a very small air load, have to be rugged enough to stand the strain of handling and normal tip landings. The fairing members in many places have to be reinforced to stand up under the tightening effect of dope. Many other parts would be too fragile to handle if they were designed only for the air loads.

The requirements for landing strength are more severe for training ships than for sailplanes because the training ships are often handled by students or inexperienced pilots. There are definite requirements for the different types of landing conditions that should be designed for. It is good practice to make the ship rugged in this respect for there is always a chance for a hard landing in any type of ship.

Although crash loads are difficult to determine and as there is much debate as to how far one should go in strengthening against these loads, it is apparent that some minimum requirements of strength and ruggedness are necessary to guard against injury from ordinary crack-ups. Stalled landings, head-on crack-ups, nose-over landings, etc., are some of the conditions that should be designed for. The extra weight used to strengthen against these crack-ups will be well worth while and this strengthening will give the pilot a better feeling of security.

Fuselage

The fuselage is essentially a structural member in the glider. It has no important beneficial aerodynamic purpose. The fuselage supports the pilot and the tail surfaces and transmits their loads to the wing structure. It also transmits all the loads to the landing gear in landings. These facts are the prime considerations in the fuselage design and construction. In the design of any particular fuselage they are considered along with other factors such as cost of construction, ease of repairing and maintaining, low aerodynamic drag, pilot's comfort and convenience and many detail considerations.

The primary fuselage is the simplest form of fuselage that will serve all the structural purposes. It is cheap and simple to construct. The construction takes the form of a simple frame structure which has all its members exposed to the air. Aerodynamic considerations are not very important. The material used may be either steel tubing or plywood and wood. The methods of assembly are conventional to each particular type of construction.

In all other types of gliders the aerodynamic drag is important. The importance of drag increases progressively from the secondary to the high performance sailplane. The drag is to be considered in the choice of type of construction. The trussed framework or box type is inferior to the stressed-skin or monocoque type because it cannot be made to conform to the pilot's shape as effectively as the monocoque type, resulting in a larger cross-section area. The monocoque type can also be made to approach the best streamlined form and have minimum skin friction. Hence for sailplanes of the highest performance class the monocoque type is used.

It is well to keep in mind the relative importance of the fuselage drag. The difference in drag between a well-faired frame fuselage and a streamlined monocoque fuselage is not very great and the fuselage drag is only part of the total drag of the glider. For this reason the frame type fuselage can be used successfully on intermediate sailplanes and sailplanes as well as on secondaries and utilities. For utility and secondary fuselages, simple fairing is sufficient. It is more important to have a clean fuselage without exposed struts, projections or openings, if possible, than to take a great deal of care with the fairing. Also because the monocoque type is usually less sturdy and more difficult to repair it is used principally on high performance sailplanes where it will receive more careful handling by experienced pilots.

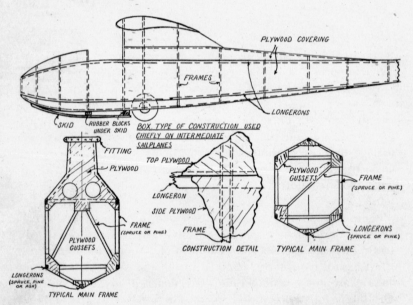

WOOD AND PLYWOOD BOX TYPE FUSELAGE CONSTRUCTION

The frame type can be built either in wood or metal. In European practice, wooden framework structure is used with plywood covering. There are no true fairing members, the sides are flat with a "V" bottom and top to form a diamond-shaped cross-section. This type is used with various minor changes such as rounded tops and

different types of cabanes for wing attachment. The plywood covering carries some stress as tension load in the framework bays, as
no diagonals are used. The frames are built of pine, spruce or ash
and assembled with plywood gussets. The longerons are also of
spruce, pine or ash. Birch, mahogany and spruce plywood are the
most commonly used. Steel fittings are bolted to the frames with
proper reinforcements to carry the loads through. If fabric covering
is used, some fairing must be provided and the bracing of the structure must be complete. Aluminum alloy also can be used, although
not much has been done with it in frame type gliders. Aluminum
alloy shapes or tubes can be used as frames with aluminum sheet
or fabric covering. The fastening must be limited to rivets, bolts
and screws, as welding is not applicable.

In American practice some use is made of the wooden types of
construction, but in general the welded steel tube fuselage is preferred for utilities and medium performance sailplanes. The struc-

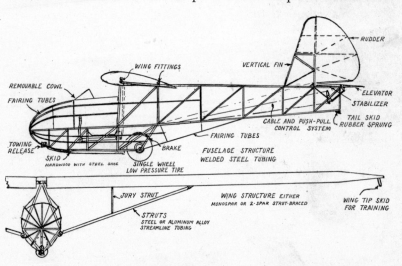

UTILITY GLIDER OF WELDED STEEL TUBE CONSTRUCTION

ture can be made more simple than the wooden frame type and
more efficient because of the better joints that are obtainable by
welding. The steel tubing is very durable and easily repaired.
Fabric covering is used and fairing members may be made of metal
tubes or formed pieces, or wood strips. The minimum sizes of tubes
specified for airplane practice do not apply but the effect of handling loads, etc., must be considered. The welder must be properly
qualified to build this type of fuselage. The proper design of joints
and fittings requires some experience in this type of design. Fittings

and control bearings, etc., are welded directly to the structure. Three or four longeron type structures or combinations of both, which may suit some designs better, are used. Standard airplane practices of protecting the tubing internally and externally are recommended.

A monocoque fuselage can be made to conform closely to the pilot's outline since there are no large structural members to inter- fere and the shape of the cross-section does not depend on any sys- tem of framework. The plywood monocoque is the type most com-

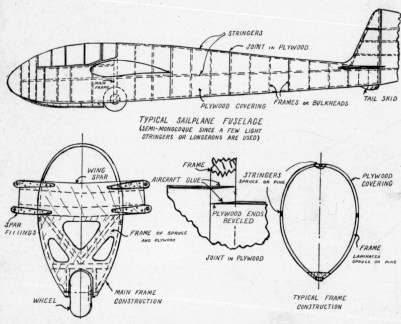

TYPICAL SAILPLANE FUSELAGE
(SEMI-MONOCOQUE SINCE A FEW LIGHT STRINGERS OR LONGERONS ARE USED)

PLYWOOD SHELL TYPE FUSELAGE CONSTRUCTION
SEMI-MONOCOQUE

monly used in sailplane construction. Actually it is a semi-mono- coque type since it always has at least three longerons or stringers. Frames or bulkheads are used to carry direct loads from the wings, landing gear and concentrated weights to the shell. Some are also used in the rear to carry the tail surfaces. Intermediate frames are made lighter as their main function is to support the shell and give the fuselage its form. Part of the efficiency of the structure is due to the fact that the shell acts as both structure and fairing. The plywood covering is applied to the frames in a series of lateral bands or rings.

On the front part of the fuselage several light stringers and longitudinal strips of plywood may be used because the smaller radius of the fuselage lines will not permit close conformity of the lateral rings. Scarf joints are used in the plywood to maintain a smooth surface. The nose piece is usually carved of wood or formed from sheet aluminum. By careful sanding and by using a rubbed paint or varnish finish, an extremely smooth surface can be obtained. In construction, the alignment of the structure is maintained by some form of jigs. Frames and bulkheads are built up of wood and plywood. Severely formed parts are laminated. Spruce, pine, birch and ash may be used for both the frames and the stringers, depending upon the designer's judgment and the materials readily available. Ash and birch are used where considerable strength and hardness are desired.

The metal monocoque fuselage has not been very extensively used in sailplanes but is rapidly becoming popular because of its strength and durability under difficult conditions and because it lends itself to forming operations more readily than plywood. Most of the types of monocoque metal construction used in powered aircraft can be applied to gliders, depending on what is desired of the fuselage. If a very light structure is desired, the use of light skin with numerous stringers and frames will be most suitable. This type of structure is more complicated since it requires a large number of parts and riveted joints. The true monocoque with heavier skin and no stringers shows promise of being very economical to build and maintain, as well as being very rugged. This type is likely to be somewhat heavier than the other. When reasonable production is possible this type of construction may be applied economically to ships of the lower performance class.

The boom type of fuselage which uses a metal tube for the rear part of the structure has found some application. This type has the advantage of considerably reduced friction drag. The metal tube itself is quite economical, but problems of simple and satisfactory attachment, and flutter may reduce its overall efficiency and economy. If a simple tube is used its section cannot easily be varied to get the maximum efficiency. The wall thickness must be relatively heavy to obtain stiffness. Tubes fabricated from sheet metal or wood are not likely to be efficient.

Wings

The complete design of a wing is a rather complex problem. It is necessary to consider aerodynamic characteristics, weight of structure, type of structure, material, ease of construction, maintenance and purpose. In general the designer avoids this complexity as much as possible by drawing on contemporary and previous practice. New gliders are rarely designed without regard for previous practice unless they are intended to serve some special or experimental purpose. The usual design is a modification of previous practice for the purpose of increasing the performance and utility, reducing the cost, or serving some special purpose. The aerodynamic design of wings is closely tied up with the structural design which definitely limits the performance obtainable.

The design of wings generally can be grouped according to the purpose for which the glider or sailplane is to be used. The grouping below indicates the usual range of construction and it is apparent that the designer has considerable leeway.

Primaries: General—2-spar, wire-braced; Occasionally—2-spar, strut-braced; Rare or Never—monospar, cantilever.

Secondaries and Utilities: General—1- or 2-spar, strut-braced; Occasionally—2-spar, wire-braced, monospar; Rare or Never—cantilever.

Intermediate Sailplanes: General—1- or 2-spar, strut-braced; Occasionally—monospar, cantilever; Rare or Never—wire bracing.

Sailplanes (high performance): General—monospar, cantilever and strut-braced monospar; Occasionally—2-spar braced; Rare or Never—wire bracing.

There are two principal classes of wing structures used in the construction of gliders and sailplanes: the monospar and the two-spar types. Multispar wings have rarely been used on gliders but might possibly be used on high performance sailplanes in metal construction. The monospar type of construction until quite recently has been almost unique to gliders. The two-spar wing is substantially the same as that used in other aircraft. Both one- and two-spar types have several variations according to type of bracing and material used.

There are general principles that apply to all types of wing construction. The wing structure must be able to withstand all types of forces that can be applied to it in its intended range of operations. Wings are not designed to be indestructible but are designed to withstand varying design loads which are determined from the purpose of the ship. The reason for using different kinds of structure is that a number of varying types of loadings exist, the proportion and magnitude of which, along with aerodynamic and cost considerations, determine which type is the most suitable.

The air forces on a wing are divided into three parts: the lifting or normal forces, the drag forces and the twisting moments about some axis along the span. In the monospar wing the lifting forces are taken by a single spar or beam. In some cases this beam may also take all the chord loads and the twisting moments. This method has been used in some airplane designs. The more common method is to use the spar and covering forward of the spar to form a D-tube which is resistant both to bending in the plane of the chord and to torsion. The ribs and skin of the wing serve the purpose of giving it the proper profile, to obtain the desired aerodynamic character- istics, and to transmit the air forces to the main structure. If they

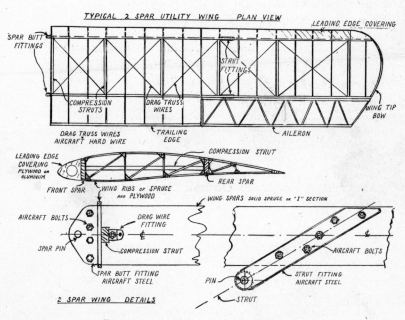

DETAILS OF TYPICAL 2-SPAR WING

can be modified to serve also as structural members, greater struc- tural efficiency is obtained. The D-tube method is used with either metal or wood construction. Another method is to use an auxiliary spar. A torsion and drag-resisting truss is built between the main spar and the auxiliary spar. This type of construction is used on powered aircraft and may find some application in gliders, especially if the rib structure can be combined with it.

In the two-spar wing the torsion loads are resolved into two loads which are applied at the front and the rear spar. The drag forces are carried between the two spars by a truss, called the drag truss. The two-spar wing is easy to build and design and is quite efficient when used on smaller spans or on relatively thin wings when large torsional loads are present. Because the spars are placed a considerable distance apart, the full depth of the airfoil section cannot be used. These two spars are never working at full efficiency at the same time because of the wide range of center of pressure travel along the chord. In two-spar wings of high aspect ratio it is necessary to use some additional means of torsion bracing, such as a double-drag truss, to give sufficient torsional rigidity. Because of this the monospar wing is used more for high aspect ratios.

The normal loads of the wing may be carried by a cantilever beam or by some form of a trussed beam using either struts or wires. The wire-braced type is used chiefly on primaries and secondaries because it is light, simple, and economical to build. However, this type is inconvenient to set up and rig and has high drag. The strut-braced or semi-cantilever type is used on secondaries, utilities and intermediate sailplanes and also on some high performance sailplanes. Streamlined struts are used: one strut on the monospar wing and two struts on the two-spar wing. There are exceptions to this, however, as two struts in the form of a "V" are sometimes used to carry torsion from a monospar wing, and one strut can be used on a two-spar wing in certain cases.

For utilities and secondaries the convenience of setting up a strut-braced ship more than compensates for any additional weight or cost. There is considerable variation in the design of strut-bracing. With the relatively thin airfoils (about 12%) used on utilities, long struts with short overhangs are used to obtain low bending moments in the spars. This requires the use of jury struts to keep the weight of the struts down. For monospar wings a slight increase in thickness permits the use of a longer overhang and a shorter strut without a jury. This gives about the ultimate simplicity in setting up, and efficiency as well. The same general design is used on many intermediate sailplanes and on some high performance sailplanes.

On normal sailplanes the use of a considerably thinner airfoil for the braced monospar than for the cantiliver wing gives both types about equal efficiency. The weight difference between the two is slight. The struts are subjected to high compression stresses and are quite heavy unless bulky sections are used. Additional fittings are also required for the struts. For general convenience in construction and operation struts are used on practically all the intermediate sailplanes while both struts and cantilever are almost equally used on high performance sailplanes. Sailplanes designed for high cruising speeds may use thin, high aspect ratio, cantilever wings. The high wing loadings of this type permit the use of heavy construction necessary for thin wings.

Biplane gliders have not been used extensively. Early training types were sometimes biplanes because very low wing loadings could be obtained with relatively small spans. Modern biplane gliders are rare. The biplane has a theoretical advantage because for a given span a biplane may have less induced drag than a monoplane. The bracing system necessary for a biplane usually will have more drag than the monoplane bracing. However, the biplane may also be built with cantilever wing construction. In general there are no serious limitations to the span of gliders and the added complications of attaching and constructing two wings do not favor the

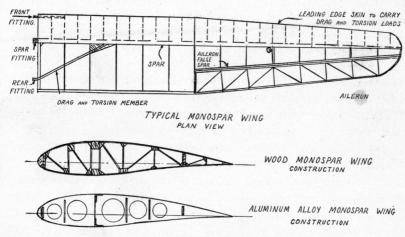

TYPICAL MONOSPAR WING
PLAN VIEW

MONOSPAR WING CONSTRUCTION

development of the biplane. The construction of the wings may be of wood or metal with the usual variations of design.

There are numerous plan forms used on glider wings, the choice again depending upon the purpose of the design. The elliptical wing has the best aerodynamic efficiency because it has the minimum induced drag. For sailplanes the elliptical cantilever wing has been used extensively. A more thorough study shows that a tapered wing gives better overall efficiency, the result of combined aerodynamic and structural efficiency. A third type using straight center sections and tapered tips gives nearly the same overall efficiency as the tapered wing and has the advantage of greater simplicity of construction. It is widely used on standard type sailplanes and is also the most frequently used type on intermediate sailplanes.

In some designs the plan form is modified by increasing the chord of the ailerons to obtain better control at the cost of some efficiency. The rectangular wing is used on primaries because it is the easiest to construct. The tips of the rectangle are usually modified, as this can be done quite readily. Secondaries and utilities also use the straight wing but higher aspect ratios are used and more care is taken with the tips to obtain better performance.

The choice of plan form is influenced to a greater degree by structural and practical considerations than by aerodynamic efficiency. Well established data show that at an aspect ratio of about 7, as commonly used on utilities, the difference in induced drag between the rectangular wing and the elliptical wing is less than 60% and the resulting difference in drag for the total glider would be considerably less. Moreover, this difference can be reduced further by modifying the shape of the tips and by using some "washout," which would leave the elliptical wing an advantage of about 2% or 3% in aerodynamic efficiency. The effect would be about twice as great for aspect ratios of 16 to 20. Tapered wings and wings with straight center sections and tapered tips closely approach the efficiency of the elliptical wing. Thus, as pointed out before, the structural and practical considerations will easily outweigh the rather small aerodynamical advantages of the elliptical wing.

The value of gull wing design has caused much discussion. Its main feature is that it gives increased wing-tip ground clearance without using dihedral over the entire span. From a structural viewpoint it is rather an undesirable complication. Its advantages for stability cannot possibly be great and the current trend of wing design has veered away from the gull wing form to that of simple dihedral.

In detail design the two-spar wing is similar to the airplane wing. In general it is lighter and simpler in construction. The spars may be of either wood or metal; solid wood for lower performance types and I-beams or box beams for the higher performance types. It is permissible to use deeper and thinner spars than in airplanes. The drag truss may be built up of either wood or hard-wire bracing. A system of double wood bracing is used on some designs, giving a very rigid wing. The hard wires may also be used double to improve the torsional rigidity of the wing. The ribs are usually of the truss type using spruce with plywood gussets. Plywood web types are rather heavy and expensive and are not extensively used. Stamped aluminum ribs are light and economical to produce commercially because less labor is required. Welded steel ribs of special design also have been used on some gliders. Leading edges usually are covered with plywood or sheet aluminum for about 10% of the chord; or false ribs and a leading edge former may be used.

Aircraft carbon steel and chrome-molybdenum steel are used for fittings. Duraluminum is also used where extreme lightness is desired but is not as satisfactory as steel if subjected to hard use. Airplane practice should be followed in the use of hard wires, cables, bolts, shackles, turnbuckles and other standard parts. Wood and plywood should be of aircraft specification. Species of wood other than spruce may be used if of proper quality, particularly

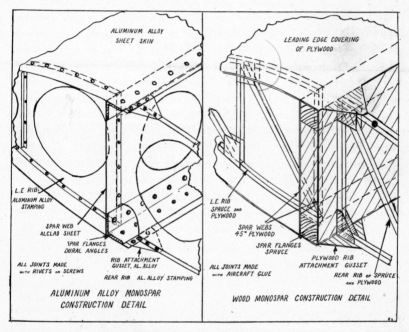

ALUMINUM ALLOY
SHEET SKIN

LEADING EDGE COVERING
OF PLYWOOD

L.E RIB
ALUMINUM ALLOY
STAMPING

L.E. RIB
SPRUCE AND
PLYWOOD

SPAR WEB
ALCLAD SHEET

SPAR WEBS
45° PLYWOOD

SPAR FLANGES
DURAL ANGLES

SPAR FLANGES
SPRUCE

ALL JOINTS MADE
WITH RIVETS OR SCREWS

RIB ATTACHMENT
GUSSET, AL. ALLOY

PLYWOOD RIB
ATTACHMENT GUSSET

REAR RIB AL. ALLOY STAMPING

ALL JOINTS MADE
WITH AIRCRAFT GLUE

REAR RIB OF SPRUCE
AND PLYWOOD

ALUMINUM ALLOY MONOSPAR
CONSTRUCTION DETAIL

WOOD MONOSPAR CONSTRUCTION DETAIL

DETAILS OF METAL AND WOOD MONOSPARS

on training ships where very low cost is desired. High strength aluminum alloys are reliable and of good quality if obtained from proper sources. The use of commercial steels for fittings is not of sufficient advantage to make it worth risking. Good aircraft steels are reasonably priced and the quality required for the average glider is quite small.

Plywood is an important factor in the monospar wood wing. The spar is invariably either a box or I-beam. The ribs are made in two sections, the front and rear, as the spar is made the full depth of the airfoil. The rear ribs are cantilever, transmitting their loads directly to the spar. An auxiliary spar may be used to support the ailerons and to take the rear drag fitting, but not to take any beam loads. The torsion and drag loads may be taken by a fitting at the leading edge or by a rear drag fitting on the auxiliary spar or diagonal brace. The D-tube is built up by covering the front section with plywood glued to the ribs and spar with casein glue. A light wood stringer is used in the leading edge to support the plywood. In some designs more stringers are used with thinner plywood. The D-tube does not permit direct accurate mathematical analysis of its strength. The designer must have some data upon which to base the design. Structural tests are necessary to determine the strength of the complete structure.

The D-tube, monospar construction lends itself well to metal construction. Stamped aluminum ribs are used with aluminum alloy sheet instead of plywood. The spar can be constructed of sheet for the web and extruded sections for the flanges as in airplane practice. Joints are made with rivets, screws or bolts, depending on the location. The self-tapping sheet metal screws are extremely useful as they give strong joints that can be opened easily for repairs. They are also very valuable in places where it is difficult to buck rivets. For very lightly loaded wings, the wood wings may have a slight weight advantage because the low density of plywood makes it relatively stiff for its weight. In structures that are more heavily loaded, the greater density of the metal permits it to be used more efficiently than the wood. Because of its many advantages, metal construction is rapidly becoming popular, as it is in airplane construction.

Ailerons

The ailerons are more uniform in design than other major parts of gliders and sailplanes. A much larger percentage of aileron area is used than on airplanes. Primaries use simple ailerons without balancing or differential action. On all other types some form of differential is used between the two ailerons. Maneuverability is a very important factor in soaring flight and it is desirable to obtain it with a minimum of loss in efficiency. The simple aileron has high adverse yawing (turning) moments, especially at high angles of attack. This requires the use of more rudder control and gives sluggish and inefficient turns. The differential action aileron tends to reduce the adverse yawing moment.

Rigging up ailerons also helps to improve the turns. Extreme differential (using up movement only) is very effective. On sailplanes the percentage of aileron chord is usually increased toward the tip and in some designs the ailerons are extended behind the normal trailing edge line. Various types of slotted and Frise ailerons exist but are not used extensively on sailplanes. Static and aerodynamic balance are used in a few designs but do not seem to be necessary except in some of the larger designs. It is, however, advantageous to keep the control forces as low as possible to avoid pilot fatigue and to make the controls responsive to a light touch. The aileron gap requires some sort of fairing as an open gap will cause drag and inefficient operation of the ailerons. This of course does not apply to the slotted or Frise type ailerons which require a definitely proportioned gap.

In wings of large span two control horns are used on the ailerons to reduce twisting loads. If the wing structure is likely to be rather flexible the ailerons are made in two separate parts to avoid binding of the hinges. The two parts may move together or may have a differential action between them.

An auxiliary false spar is frequently used to carry the aileron hinges and the necessary gap fairing. In the two-spar wing construction, the proportion of the aileron and the position of the spar often makes the false spar unnecessary. Some monospar designs use cantilever hinge brackets to carry the aileron loads to the main spar and D-tube. The false spar may be supported by reinforced ribs or by special brackets.

Two types of aileron construction are commonly used. In one type the ribs carry the only direct aerodynamic load to the torsion member. The control horn is mounted directly on the torsion member which also acts as the beam to carry all the shear loads to the hinges. The other type uses a spar which is not resistant to torsion, to carry the shear loads. The ribs are arranged to form a truss to carry through the torsion loads to the control horn. The first type is adaptable to long narrow ailerons and to balanced ailerons of the slotted and Frise type where it is desirable to concentrate the weight of the aileron near the front. The second type gives a lighter structure and is used more extensively. The materials, as in the rest of the wing structure, may be of wood, plywood or metal. Various other types exist, such as metal or plywood box types and others with different type of torsion bracing and details. Hinges may be of the conventional airplane type. Aluminum alloy piano hinges can be used to advantage in eliminating the gap, the hinge being used on the upper surface of the wing.

Rotating wing tip ailerons have been used on some gliders but are rarely used on any new designs. These ailerons are adapted to sailplanes with long tapered tips. Installation is made directly on the control torque tube which also acts as a cantilever beam. The tip aileron is easily susceptible to damage on the ground and in general does not compare with the conventional type aileron in efficiency and effectiveness.

Wing Fuselage Connections

In sailplane design the wing and fuselage connection is rather important as it is a great source of drag and disturbance if not designed properly. The earliest types of sailplanes used the high wing exclusively to permit more depth for the strut bracing and to keep the wings away from the ground. When the wing is just set on the fuselage the interference drag is high. The connection is more efficient when the high wing is set on a neck or cabane extending up from the fuselage. Cabanes consisting of a number of small supporting struts have considerably more drag than the full fuselage cabane.

Numerous tests in wind tunnels have shown that the midwing and shoulder wing installation have the least interference drag. Sufficient depth for struts can usually be obtained with the shoulder wing and a much more rigid fastening of the wing to the fuselage is obtained with the mid- or shoulder wing than with the high wing. The fittings can be fastened directly to the large parts of the frames or bulkheads, giving greater strength.

Mid-wing and shoulder-wing types are more likely to cause burbling and buffeting of the tail surfaces, and fillets are usually required at the junction of the wing and fuselage. The exact type of filleting required can be determined accurately beforehand only by wind tunnel tests. There are, however, considerable data available which will give the designer a good idea of the best design.

Tail Surfaces

The tail surfaces of gliders usually are conventional with many minor variations in design used by individual designers. On normal ships a stabilizer and fin are used, but in the past none were used on high performance sailplanes and in some cases even on training ships. In the case of the sailplane the undamped surfaces (those without fixed stabilizer areas) were used to obtain very responsive controls but in training gliders the only advantage was ease of construction. It is now the general practice to use a stabilizer and some fin area on practically all sailplanes and gliders. Higher speeds and blind flying require more stability and make this necessary. Adequate maneuverability is obtained on sailplanes with a stabilizer and it is required for safety on training ships. The fin area is of lesser importance as the fuselage has some fin effect, but it is required in some designs to obtain the desired stability.

The most important requirements of the tail surfaces are that they give satisfactory maneuverability and stability with the minimum amount of drag. Ease of assembly is quite important and construction must be considered. Cantilever surfaces are used on practically all sailplanes while strut-braced surfaces are used on most intermediate types. Wires and struts are used on primaries, secondaries and utilities. Aerodynamic balance is frequently used on rudders and on some elevators. Static balance has been applied to a few of the larger sailplanes for elevators and rudders.

The undamped type of elevator most used is the balanced cantilever type. It is made in two halves mounted on either end of the torque tube running through the fuselage. The torque tube also carries all the cantilever loads of the elevator. If this type is used care should be taken to see that the torque tube and its bearings are free from play and rugged enough to withstand reasonable handling loads. The position of the torque tube must not be too far back as aerodynamic overbalance can cause dangerous conditions. It might be repeated here that it is now considered good practice to use a damped horizontal control surface on all gliders.

The arrangement of tail surfaces varies with designer and type of glider. They are perhaps best discussed in groups. In sailplanes external horns, wires, struts and fittings are to be avoided. It is desirable to keep the torsion loads about the fuselage due to the tail surfaces as low as possible. The horizontal surfaces are usually made in two parts, permitting the rudder centroid to be near the fuselage axis. The rudder area is also disposed so that the centroid is as low as possible. The elevator axis is usually placed a short distance ahead of the rudder axis permitting an internal horn on the connecting torque member of the elevators. The stabilizer is usually cantilever in construction, the rear span carrying all the beam loads and the resulting torsion loads being carried through by the stabilizer ribs. The stabilizer leading edge member is usually too shallow to act as a beam. In some designs a spar is used some distance to the rear of the leading edge. Similar arrangements are used in which the rear stabilizer spar is strut-braced. This is often used in the intermediate sailplanes.

A new American version uses a joint in the elevator torque member in line with the pins of the stabilizer spar and leading edge. This permits the horizontal tail surfaces to be folded up against the fin by releasing the stabilizer strut pin. The construction of the surfaces may be of wood, aluminum alloy or steel tubing. For cantilever surfaces wood or aluminum alloy are best adapted. Steel tubing is used extensively because of the ease of construction by welding, but it is rather heavy. Remarkably light surfaces can be constructed of aluminum alloy formed sections.

On primaries and secondaries the surfaces are usually wire-braced, permitting simple sections, such as small tubing and solid wood sections, to be used in the construction. Two separate elevators are usually used and may be controlled by separate cables or by a torque tube with the horn slightly offset from the fuselage. Various systems have been devised to speed up assembly of the control surfaces, particularly on utilities where quick assembly is important. In some designs the fin and the rudder are removable and in others they remain on the fuselage in trailing, the fin being arranged so that the stabilizer is readily removable.

Another type that has found application on all types of gliders, as well as on airplanes, has the fin and rudder set ahead of the horizontal tail surfaces. This permits the use of a one-piece elevator and simplifies construction and assembly of the tail surfaces. On some sailplanes the resulting high position of the rudder is objectionable due to the large twisting moment on the fuselage. There have been some failures of this type of rudder but they have been due to poor detail design rather than to the design principles. Cantilever or strut-braced types are used for the fixed surfaces as the position of the fin and rudder is not convenient for wire bracing. If the dimensions of the tail surfaces are kept low enough the surfaces may be left installed on the fuselage for trailing. If the span of the surfaces exceeds 7 feet, more care is required in trailing and on longer trips it is safer to remove them.

In addition to the air loads, the tail surfaces are designed to withstand handling loads, and some form of tail skid assembly usually is necessary to protect the rudder from damage on landings and take-offs. Wire bracing is susceptible to damage in heavy grass or on landing in farm crops. Design loads for the stress analysis will usually give smaller wire sizes than it is practical to use. In strut-braced and cantilever surfaces care is necessary in designing the assembly fittings so that there will be no play. Play will permit vibration or flutter of the tail surfaces at high speeds or in some condition in which a burble is set up by the wing or the fuselage. Severe buffeting of the tail surfaces due to fuselage and wing burbling must be corrected at its origin and not at the tail surfaces. Large spoilers and flaps may also cause some vibration of the tail surfaces. This usually occurs only briefly and is not serious unless it is very severe.

Control Systems

The control system is an essential part of any aircraft and in the design of a glider it is important that the design and installation of the controls be carefully considered. Reliability and ease of control are the most important considerations. Simplicity in design will do much to attain reliability and ease of operation.

Control cables are the simplest and most efficient means of transmitting control forces for most installations. For short lengths the use of push-pull tubes or torque tubes is often more satisfactory. For relatively long controls such as aileron controls, the push-pull tubes will be heavier than cables, but considerations of quick connection in setting up, ease of installation and long life often favor the use of tubes.

In order to attain reliability in the control system, only proper quality of materials should be used. Aircraft standard cables, bolts, pins, turnbuckles and other small parts should be used. Aircraft sheet steel and tubing are also recommended for control systems. It is advisable to follow good airplane practice in detail design. This includes the selection of proper sizes of cables and tubes for all installations. Hard wire has been used frequently for control wire but this is very bad practice and should not be permitted. Torque tubes should have sleeves at bearing points and at points where horns are welded on, unless large margins of safety are present. All joints and pins require adequate bearing area for strength and wear. Cable splicing should conform to aircraft practice and all controls should have stops.

The detail design and installation of control systems vary so widely that it is not within the scope of this chapter to cover them all. In general the controls are similar to aircraft controls. Rudder bars or pedals of various types and construction are used with cables running directly to the rudder horns with as few pulleys and fairleads as possible. The stick control is used for most gliders except that in some sailplanes the wheel or "dep" control is used. The wheel permits the use of a narrower fuselage cross-section and in large sailplanes with heavy control forces it is useful because of the greater mechanical advantage that it permits.

The control stick is usually mounted on a fore-and-aft torque tube which operates the ailerons. The stick is pivoted on the torque tube for elevator movement. Cables or push-pull tubes are used to transmit the control forces to the elevators. Another type of installation has the torque tube across the fuselage. The stick is pivoted on the torque tube for aileron control forces which are carried by cable. The torque tube transmits the elevator control forces by cable or push-pull tube. Wheel controls are generally mounted on a small column which moves fore and aft for elevator control. The airplane type of wheel coming through the dash panel has not been used mainly because of installation difficulties.

The method of transmitting the control forces from the stick and torque tube to the control surfaces varies in practice. In sailplanes and utility wings a closed wire system is usually used. The aileron cables end at the wing butt, on an idler horn which is connected by a link to a bell crank on the fuselage. Thus the ailerons can be disconnected by the removal of two pins. This eliminates the necessity of adjusting the ailerons when reassembling the ship. The same thing can be accomplished by the use of a pull-push tube and bell crank system. The fuselage idler horn is connected to the stick or torque tube by a cable or push-pull tube system. Primaries commonly use a closed wire system from the ailerons to the control stick, or torque tube. While this system takes longer to set up and rig, it is used because of its simplicity and low cost.

Elevators may be connected directly from the stick to the elevator horns by a single tube with proper guides to permit the use of reasonable light tubes. Cables are more often used for the elevators than the tubes, however. The cables may be connected directly to the elevator horns or to an idler horn and then to the elevator horn by a link tube. When two separate elevators are used they may be connected by separate cables or link tubes or by the methods described before.

In all closed cable systems the linkage must be correct to avoid loosening or tightening of the cable system due to unequal displacements of the horns. Quadrant type horns are superior to the ordinary horn as they have a constant effective radius but are not absolutely necessary except in special cases. They are used where large angular displacements are necessary or if the direction of the cable must be changed by a pulley close to a horn. The differential action of aileron control is obtained by offsetting the idler horn on the fuselage in favor of the up aileron. If extreme differential action is desired this may be done by offsetting another horn: either the horn at the stick or in the wing at the ailerons. In using differential linkage it should be borne in mind that large forces can be built up in the control system. The effect and magnitude of these forces must be considered carefully.

As mentioned before, the arrangement of the control system to facilitate rapid assembly is important. The use of push-pull tubes and idler horns and link tubes is useful for this purpose and also to eliminate the possibility of crossed controls. Where elevator or ailerons are connected in setting up a glider it is advisable to use some device to make sure that the cables cannot be crossed. Pins of different sizes and different types of end connections for each part will help prevent this from happening. A simple precaution of this type is well worth while as serious accidents have been caused by crossed controls.

Plain bearings for the control system are quite satisfactory if reasonable care is taken with the design. If the glider is likely to get extensive use, the use of removable bushings and other means of eliminating play is desirable. Ball and roller bearings may be used in all control joints and hinges to reduce friction and insure long life. Grit and dust are a menace to plain bearings because it is difficult to prevent their entry at the oil holes and other openings. This grit will cause scratches that may be deep enough to affect the strength of a thin walled tube. For this reason sleeves are recommended for bearing points. Ball bearings are available with dust shields and a permanent lubrication supply. This eliminates the entry of grit and the necessity of frequent lubrications. The cost of ball bearings is higher than plain bearings but it is not excessive.

DETAIL DESIGN CONSIDERATIONS

One not familiar with glider and sailplane design might think that once the general aerodynamic and structural design is decided upon, the rest is of a more or less routine nature not requiring any special design consideration. But such is not the case. The design and arrangement of the details such as releases, controls, cockpits, landing gears, etc., are special problems in themselves, requiring much thought and consideration. The type and the purpose of the sailplane are determining factors in the detail design, as are efficiency, safety, economy and simplicity. All these things must be considered together with what is considered good practice in designing these parts.

In European countries where soaring is more advanced, engineers have developed special designs for parts that must be conformed to. Releases, safety belts and fittings are some of the details that have become standardized. This may tend to stifle inventiveness and development, but it does result in safer and more uniform operations. This idea could well be followed in the United States on a more liberal scale.

Actually the whole design of a sailplane or glider can be broken down into details, but we will be concerned with the more obvious ones—those that are more open to change: releases, cockpit design, extra control devices, landing gear, fitting and assembly features and trailers.

Towing Releases and Hooks

A number of years ago when shock-cord launching was practically the only type used, all gliders were equipped with nose hooks which served as a means of launching and towing on the ground. This hook of simple open type was mounted on the nose of the glider. It was inclined backwards so that when there was tension on the cord the ring would slide up into a rounded notch at the top. When the tension of the cord was released, the ring slid down and fell off. Other types of launches have almost completely replaced the shock-cord method and most ships now do not even have a nose hook. However, as there are still sites where shock-cord launching is necessary, this method is not completely eliminated from use. It is possible to use the release hook for this type of launching, but there is some chance of trouble if the pilot does not release at the right time.

In designing the nose hook, ruggedness and wear must be considered along with the strength required. It must be rugged enough to withstand rough usage and side loads encountered in launching and ground towing. The minimum design load generally used is a 2400-pound pull forward, diverging as much as 14° in any direction from a straight line through the nose hook and point of hold-back. This is a considerable load and represents the maximum possible with four strands of ⅝-inch cord at 100% elongation (with a safety factor). This is the tension design load for the hook, attachment and usually for the front of the fuselage. The position of the hook is important for proper operation. It should be placed where there is no chance of the ring or cord catching in some part of the fuselage when it drops off.

When auto towing replaced shock-cord launching, many types of hooks and voluntary releases were designed. The ordinary nose hook was unsatisfactory for towing as it was difficult and sometimes impossible to release when desired and was generally unreliable. The ring also had a tendency to fall off in flight and in towing on the ground. The essential principle of a release is that of a hook that can be opened at the will of the pilot. The importance of proper operation can readily be seen, yet there were many poor designs that failed to open or "jammed." In many European countries the type of release has been standardized, but in the

United States no standard has been set and many types are being used.

In Germany there is only one standard type of release allowed for glider, tow plane or car. This is known as the DLV release and is the result of extensive research and experience with many types of releases. Its main feature is that it will operate regardless of the position of the towrope, and that its opening does not depend upon the tension of the rope. The release is really composed of two parts: the two links and the release mechanism itself. The two oval metal links are of different size, the larger being attached to the towrope. The smaller one fits horizontally into the jaws of the release and the larger rests against a metal ring welded to the front of the release. This allows the rope to go in any position without any tendency to jam the jaws. The positive release instead of the usual tension type insures the ejecting of the rings regardless of whether there is any tension on the rope or not. So the only possibility of failure would be to have the actuating mechanism between the release and the pilot fail. As this is of simple and straightforward design, such a possibility is remote.

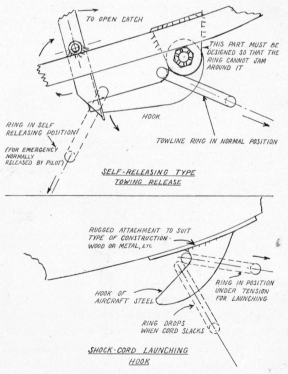

TO OPEN CATCH

THIS PART MUST BE DESIGNED SO THAT THE RING CANNOT JAM AROUND IT

HOOK

RING IN SELF RELEASING POSITION!

(FOR EMERGENCY NORMALLY RELEASED BY PILOT)

TOWLINE RING IN NORMAL POSITION

SELF-RELEASING TYPE TOWING RELEASE

RUGGED ATTACHMENT TO SUIT TYPE OF CONSTRUCTION· WOOD OR METAL, ETC

HOOK OF AIRCRAFT STEEL

RING IN POSITION UNDER TENSION FOR LAUNCHING

RING DROPS WHEN CORD SLACKS

SHOCK-CORD LAUNCHING HOOK

TOWING RELEASE AND SHOCK-CORD HOOK

One type very popular in this country, with an advantage over other types, is the release that opens itself when there is any back pull on the rope. This feature is very valuable when the towline fails to release due to mechanical failure, jamming or pilot error. The release is generally the same as other types except that the hook and release trip are placed so that when the line of action of the towrope is to the rear, the ring slides down the hook and releases itself. This type does not have the positive release, but its necessity is questioned by many. In almost all cases the tension required to open the hook is exceedingly small and usually can be accomplished by the weight of the ring and a few feet of the towline. In the release above, this can be accomplished sometimes by the weight of the hook itself. The one advantage that the DLV release has over this type is that it will open from any angle of the towline. Most self-releasing types will not open readily from direct side pull but this condition is seldom if ever experienced and can be corrected by changing the position of the ship.

There are many different types of releases being used. Many use the principle of a pivoted hook with a catch that holds the hook closed. When the release is pulled the catch opens and the tension on the rope rotates the hook and throws out the ring. As the main requirement for releases is that they function properly at the right time for all conditions, these last three items should be considered.

The position of the release on the glider is important, as it can affect the loads put on a ship to a large degree. The general design makes it easy and convenient to put the release on the front or underside of the nose, corresponding to the skid end of a primary glider. This has proven to be the best place as it has the effect of damping the action of the wings and tail surface. If the release position is moved toward the center of gravity this damping effect become less, towing becomes unstable and it is possible to put large loads on the ship. Clearance of the rope and ring after releasing is important. The fuselage around the release should be clear of any obstructions that might catch the rope or ring.

As most releases will be used for shock-cord launching some time or other, they should be designed for these loads. This tension condition will more than cover those of airplane and auto tow and usually designs the front of the fuselage for tension. Design loads for winch and auto tow depend upon the general size and features of the ship and upon the towing speed. These loads should be investigated thoroughly because they are surprisingly high and side loads must be accounted for to insure ruggedness.

Cockpit

In cockpit design the main motive should be one of safety and efficiency. It is the control point of the ship and houses the pilot. In the past designers have not given much consideration to the pilot's safety and comfort or to making the cockpit attractive. They were concerned with improving performance and cutting down the fuselage area and drag. Now the value of pilot efficiency and comfort is realized and it is becoming the designing factor. The effect of a comfortable upholstered cabin or cockpit on the skeptical observer is also being realized. It gives a feeling of security quite different from that given by seeing a pilot mixed in with a mass of structural tubes or sitting out on the "front porch" of an open primary.

Clarence Lee Dale

A Plexiglas Cockpit Cover on a Sailplane

The question of open or closed type of cockpit depends to a large extent upon the type and purpose of the ship. Closed cabins are used on sailplanes to improve performance and to protect the pilot. They are not used on training ships because the feel and sound of the air stream is one of the important aids to the beginner. In the closed type, flying has to be done mainly by feel of the controls and by instruments. Many models are fitted with convertible cowls so that both types can be used on one ship.

In all types of ships, visibility is important for safe flying. In sailplanes, extra visibility is necessary for cloud and thermal soaring, especially in the upward quadrant, and the present trend is toward larger and clearer cabins. Molded types of transparent enclosures give the best aerodynamic form but usually are expensive and difficult to form. Flat celluloid sheets are most commonly used and they result in a reasonably smooth section if small enough segments are used. Cockpit enclosures should be made to open quickly to permit leaving the ship rapidly in an emergency. The attaching hooks or snaps should be of the positive type so that there is no danger of their opening unless actually operated by the pilot. Suitable ventilation control should be provided as an enclosed cabin tends to get hot and stuffy. Colored top for transparent covers will help keep the glare down.

Hans Groenhoff

CLOSE-UP OF COCKPITS OF SCHWEIZER TWO-SEATER

The cockpits and cabins should not contain any sharp corners that one might bump against in a crack-up or a hard landing. All edges should be suitably padded and covered over. The instrument board should be smooth and padded where one might hit oneself. Windshield edges and cowling edges should be taped with binding or some similar material. Head and back pads should also be provided. A well-padded cockpit can do a lot to reduce injuries sustained in crack-ups.

On most gliders and intermediate sailplanes the stick control is used almost exclusively, while in sailplanes, where small outside dimensions are desired, the compact "dep" or wheel control is widely used. Other "trick" types of controls have appeared but even if they have many advantages they are not used much because of the difficulty of getting pilots to change from one to the other. Rudder pedals have almost completely replaced the rudder bar, except in primaries, because of the ease of installation and operation. There is little choice in the placement of these controls except perhaps that the height of the rudder pedals is variable.

The design and shape of the seat is an important item for comfort and efficient flying. People's tastes vary greatly as to the design of a seat, but the fundamental thing is to get the weight distributed so that no one part of the body carries too much weight. As parachutes are worn for most soaring flights, their size and weight must be considered. In training ships there is not much use for parachutes as almost all the flights are under the minimum height requirement for proper operation of the parachute. But in sailplanes it is the practice to wear one and it is required for airplane towing, cloud flying and aerobatic flying. Provision is best made for them in the seat. When one is not worn the well in the seat can be filled up with cushions. The safety belt should be of the approved type and fastened to the main structure of the fuselage so that the full strength of the belt can be developed.

Release, spoiler, flap, brake and any other specialized controls should be placed in convenient positions so that they may be operated easily and not confused. The release control is usually a ring placed prominently on the dash. As we are accustomed to a lever for the brake, it is best if this can be carried out for brakes on gliders. Spoilers are sometimes coupled with the brake so that they work together. It is necessary to hold the spoiler when first touching the ground, for if it is closed the lift will build up again and the glider may take off. So, in order to stop short, both the spoiler and the brake must be operated at the same time while controlling the ship. Flap controls must be of the irreversible type; that is, designed so that loads on the flap cannot be carried back to the control handle. This is to prevent a sudden gust or an increase in load from taking the control out of the pilot's hand and closing the flap. Other controls should be placed in accordance with their importance and operating requirements.

As instruments are playing an increasingly important part in soaring, the instrument boards are getting larger. Thermal soaring and blind flying in clouds require almost steady instrument flying and so the board in sailplanes must be placed where it can best be seen without cutting down visibility. Other design considerations of the cockpit also limit the position of the instrument panel. It should be made so that it is easy to maintain and remove. In sailplanes, provision should be made for extra equipment carried for long flights and contest and record attempts. A special compartment with padding mounts should be provided for the barograph. Room should be provided for maps, navigation equipment, radio, food, supplies, tools, camera, first-aid kit and other equipment used on a long flight. Oxygen equipment is necessary to exceed the altitude records.

Extra Control Devices

The modern sailplane has become so efficient that at times this feature becomes a distinct disadvantage. With the high gliding ratios and low sinking speeds it is a difficult problem to bring a sailplane into a small field without the use of abnormal maneuvers or special control devices. There are also times when it is desirable to change the aerodynamic characteristics in flight in order to increase or decrease efficiency, cruising speed, sinking speed or gliding ratio. The use of extra controls for this purpose is just beginning and it offers great possibilities for improving sailplane performance.

As all these control devices involve aerodynamics to a large degree, they must be considered first from this angle. It is dangerous to experiment without proper investigation as to the effect of the controls upon the balance, strength, and aerodynamic features of the sailplane. This is especially true when the controls are large in size and hence may become powerful. Many of these devices disturb the normal airflow, setting up disturbances that may induce flutter in other components of the ship. Some tend to change the balance of the ship and set up local loads that may prove troublesome. These effects can be predicted and calculated quite closely and so should be investigated thoroughly.

The need for devices to help sailplanes land is quite apparent. If one comes in too high it must be slipped, fishtailed, or put through some other maneuvers to use up its potential energy. These are rather difficult in large-span sailplanes. With the use of special devices these maneuvers can be eliminated and their effect much improved and better controlled. One of the first attempts at landing control was the use of split flaps. The effect of these flaps is to increase the lift (decrease the landing speed) and increase the drag with resulting decrease in gliding ratio. This was not quite what was wanted for good landing control as the ships of that time had very low landing speeds to begin with, and the lessened speed resulted in sloppy controls and made them difficult to land in a strong wind or rough air. However, with the rapid increase of wing loadings and the use of flaps for variable airfoil effect, full trailing edge flaps now have a definite place on sailplanes to decrease landing speed and to improve performance.

In order to get better landing control, the spoiler was developed. The duty of the spoiler is to decrease or "spoil" the lift and to increase the drag, hence decreasing the gliding ratio and increasing the landing speed. The spoilers are plates on top of each wing that cause the lift to break down and the drag to increase over that section. Their total area is usually around 1% of the wing area and their aspect ratio from 4 to 8. They are more practical than flaps because they offer better control with no tricky features. They can be put on or off at will without any change of balance and any danger of spilling. Because of this they are applicable for training ships where the necessity for a quick landing often precedes the pilot's ability to slip or maneuver the ship properly.

The optimum size, position and aspect ratio are controversial, as not much research has been done along this line. They usually are placed near the 30% point of the wing chord although the present tendency seems to be to put them back a bit farther. Their position along the span is of importance as they must be placed so that turbulence from them does not affect the ailerons or tail surfaces. It is best to have them in as far as possible so that if one of them should become inoperative in flight, no great difference in banking or turning moment would be experienced. As they are usually placed where the pressure on the wing is lowest they have a tendency to come open in flight. They should be designed so that this will not happen as it naturally has a bad effect on the performance of the ship.

Another type of flap that has a place on sailplanes is the drag flap. This flap does little or nothing to the lift but increases the drag considerably. This type is also very adaptable to sailplanes because of its simplicity and desired effect of steepening the glide without appreciable increase in landing speed. This flap usually is quite a bit larger than the spoilers and is placed on the underside of the wing. Its position along the chord of the wing is not so important as long as it is kept within limits.

The spoiler and drag flap have been combined in some cases and called the double spoiler. The drag flap is placed directly under the spoiler and may work with it or independently. The effect is to decrease the lift and increase the drag considerably. This type of spoiler was designed primarily for limiting the speed of sailplanes in clouds. Due to blind flying and terrific turbulence, excessive speed is sometimes gained rapidly. With the double spoiler it is possible to increase the drag so that it limits the speed and helps prevent failures. This type of spoiler is also very useful for losing altitude quickly and to keep from being drawn up into a storm front or a cloud.

A great future lies in the use of special devices to improve the efficiency of sailplanes. The use of the adjustable stabilizer offers one-piece elevator efficiency with hands-off flying qualities. The fixed stabilizer is only efficient for one angle (or speed) and becomes an extra source of drag at high and low speeds. There is much to be gained over the fixed type and the operation mechanism is rather simple. Trimming tabs are fundamentally inefficient and should be avoided on sailplanes. By deflecting full trailing-edge flaps a bit upward it is possible to improve high speed performance, while a slight downward deflection will slightly increase the lift and efficiency. Further deflection will give normal flap action. These features are especially desirable in cross-country sailplanes where both minimum sinking speed and high cruising speed are desired.

The external airfoils offer good possibilities along this line. In this type an auxiliary airfoil is placed a little behind the trailing edge of the main wing. Its chord is usually from $\frac{1}{5}$ to $\frac{1}{10}$ of the wing chord and it is supported by brackets coming from the main wing. By varying the angle of the auxiliary airfoil the characteristics of the main wing are changed and reports show that this method is much more efficient and effective than the full flap. It offers some construction problems as it must be made accurately and the wing must be strengthened to take care of the extra torsion. For the long-distance sailplane of the future, which will have to fly fast and still have low sinking speed, it offers excellent possibilities.

Landing Gears

The early gliders and sailplanes usually were equipped with a simple elementary skid. Because of slow landing speed and light weight it was possible to make smooth landings with this type. In most installations the skid extends from the nose to a small distance behind the center of gravity. Skids are usually made of hard durable wood, sometimes covered with metal, and are easily replaceable. The "Vampyr" used soccer balls for its landing gear. This was probably the first pneumatic type of landing gear used. Instead of continuing along this line, engineers went back to the skid, and used rubber blocks, tennis balls or springs for shock absorption.

The skid type of landing gear was practical for shock-cord launchings, the extra friction of the skid making it easy to hold back the tail. It also made possible short landings, as pressure could be applied to the skid by nosing down. But with the advent of auto, winch and airplane towing there was need for a better type of landing gear. With these types of towing, the skid made it very difficult to take off because of the high ground drag. It took a lot of power to get these large sailplanes up to flying speed and tow-ropes broke frequently and skids wore out quickly.

In Germany, instead of going to landing wheels, they developed a two-wheeled cart called a "dolly" that fastened underneath the skid and was used for taking off and handling on the ground. A special fitting with a release was provided on the bottom of the fuselage and as soon as the glider took off the pilot released the dolly. This method, although reducing the drag, was not very satisfactory in training and routine flying. It is a lot of trouble to lift the ship and attach the dolly and there is always the danger that a premature release might damage the rear part of the fuselage or tail surfaces.

In the United States, wheels were introduced on training gliders and it was not long before they were used on sailplanes. They are much more convenient than a dolly and give better and easier ground performance in handling and landing. With the use of wheel brakes and the front skid, it is also possible to make very short landings. Although the original cost is higher than the skid, the cost of maintenance is very low. It has so many advantages and good features that it is considered almost a necessity, especially with the modern methods of towing.

Although both single and double type landing gears are used, the single wheel partly enclosed in the center of the fuselage is the more popular because it is simpler, cheaper and more efficient. In most cases two-wheel landing gears are awkward and add a lot of drag and weight. They have their place in training gliders where they eliminate the man who holds the tip and consequently speed up handling. In landing they also have the advantage of saving the tips from damage. With the single wheel, tip skids are often used to prevent damage of the tip but they are not absolutely necessary, for if care is used the glider can usually be brought to a full stop before the wing will drop.

There are many variations of the single-wheel type used. A prac-tical one is that with the wheel slightly behind the c.g. (center of gravity) with a simple skid in the front and a spring skid at the tail. In the normal loaded condition on the ground there is a little weight on the front skid and the rest on the wheel. This makes it convenient for handling and towing. In landing, pressure can easily be put on the front skid by nosing down, if braking of this type is desired. When the ship is empty it rests on the wheel and the tail skid with most of the weight on the former. This prevents pounding of the tail in towing back empty and makes it generally easier to handle.

Another variation of the single-wheel gear is the type with the wheel well ahead of the c.g., with only a tail skid. The absence of front skids makes the brakes very important as there is no skid to rub along the ground. This type also puts a lot of load on the tail which results in heavy handling and pounding in towing back. Probably its only advantage is its simplicity of construction due to the absence of skids and necessary supporting structure.

By moving the wheel position, the characteristics of the landing gear can be changed. The farther back the wheel is moved (up to the c.g.) the easier it is to handle on the ground, as the c.g. of the ship empty is near the axle. The farther front the wheel is moved the better it handles in towing, as the c.g. (loaded) is near the axle. The disadvantage of the first is that when moved back too far the loads on the front skid become too large. With the second, the disadvantage is that the tail and handling loads become large.

Another type used often is that with the wheel just a bit ahead of the c.g. (loaded), with a skid to the front and rear of the wheel. In both conditions the weight rests on the wheel and the rear skid with the tail skid off the ground. This type has the disadvantage of rocking about the rear skid and banging the tail when towed back empty.

Because of the high cost of self-contained wheel brakes, they have not been used much in gliders. Most types have simple elementary friction brakes that rub against the tire. A hinged paddle with a canvas shoe is often used. A spring keeps it from the wheel when not in use and a wire pull generally operates it.

The purpose and the type of ship should be considered in deciding upon the type and strength of landing gear. It is quite evident that training gliders should have more rugged installations than sailplanes. Also the question of drag is important in the higher performance types and in some cases has led to retractable landing gears. As there are usually no shock absorbing devices on gliders other than the wheel, it is important that this be large enough to take the required shock. The supporting structure should be very substantial so that the wheel will fail before the structure will be damaged. The effect of side loads on the supporting structure should be investigated. A rugged supporting structure will do away with a lot of repairing and realignment usually necessary after very hard landings.

Fitting and Assembly Details

As fittings hold together the major components of a sailplane, their importance can readily be appreciated. In designing and constructing them many things have to be considered besides the strength required to carry through the flight loads. As the wings and other parts are usually handled by the fittings in assembly, loading on trailer, etc., the fittings have to be rugged enough to take these loads. They also have to have extra margins to take care of wear caused by frequent assembly and disassembly. They have to be protected against corrosion as they are often exposed to the weather and scratched and worn off in handling. Plating is the best method of protecting against corrosion, although proper priming and painting will do if given good care. In some cases fittings are used to support the glider on the trailer. This possibility also must be considered in their design and allowances made for strength and wear.

The materials used for fittings should be strong and tough, made to aircraft specifications. Chrome-molybdenum steel is one of the most popular metals for fittings, it being a tough steel that can be welded easily. Materials which tend toward brittleness or softness should not be used. Castings for fittings are taboo unless one has equipment to guarantee their reliability and uniformity. Even then the 100% margin required for castings usually overcomes any weight advantage. The most common metal for pins is aircraft nickel-steel. This can be machined easily in the heat-treated state.

Quick and easy assembly can do a lot to take the drudgery out of setting up a ship. Of the three general types (cantilever, strut-braced and wire-braced semi-cantilever) the strut brace is usually the easiest to assemble, with the cantilever next and the wire-braced last.

In cantilever types it is the practice to use taper pins for assembly as it is necessary to hold the wings rigidly in place. Because of the long span and the closeness of fittings any play at the center fittings will be magnified many times out at the tips. The taper pins are pulled snugly into the holes by means of a locking nut. To extract them the other end is usually provided with a thread which permits the use of a puller. Cantilever wings take longer than braced wings because the taper pins require more time for proper fitting than straight pins. In a braced model the straight pins are just pushed in and locked, while in a cantilever type the taper pins have to be inserted, gradually tightened, and then locked.

In semi-cantilever design with struts it is conventional to use straight pins for fittings. Although tightness of joints is not so important as in cantilever types, it is important to have good, smooth fits. If there is a little play to start with it will quickly wear the hole larger. Regular aircraft nickel-steel bolts are often used for pins but their manufacturing tolerances sometimes result in loose fits. On strut ends, universal joints are widely used to prevent

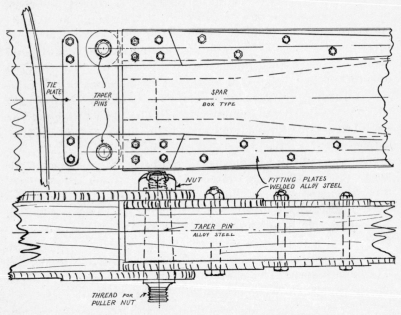

TYPICAL CANTILEVER SPAR JOINT DETAILS

damage to the fittings. They prevent side loads from being carried through the strut into the fitting.

Although putting the wings on may seem to be the main and longest job in assembly, it usually takes more time to put on the tail surfaces and hook up the various controls. Because of this, extra time spent on simplifying assembly features will be amply repaid in ease and speed of assembly. With some types it is possible to leave the horizontal tail surfaces on in trailing and with many the rudder can also stay on. However, the majority of sailplanes have to remove their tail surfaces for trailing. Folding tail surfaces are quickly coming into vogue as they simplify assembly and carrying of the surfaces. There are, however, some design and construction problems that sometimes make this type impractical. The substitution of push rods for wires or cables will also help to speed assembly, and prevent incorrect hooking up. Assembly methods and systems offer a field for clever ideas and invention, and effort along this line will not be wasted.

Trailers

The main requirement for a glider trailer is that it transport the glider or sailplane from point to point without damage. A ship being transported is liable to be damaged due to: improper loading or suspension, wind, rain, hail, and the numerous accidents of the road. How far one wants to go to protect his craft depends a lot upon its type and cost. However, there are fundamental requirements that should be observed so that no structural damage is done to the glider.

The trailer should be sprung properly so that shock and vibration will not disarrange the mountings or damage the parts. The parts should *not* be mounted so that large loads can be put through the glider structure. All parts should be held firmly in place so that no damage results from the moving or wearing of parts. The trailer must operate properly without trouble from running gear, structure, hitches or lighting equipment.

For primary and utility types the open frame type trailer is widely used. It is simple and inexpensive and is satisfactory for these types of ships. For more expensive types the covered trailers are more popular because of the added protection that they give. They are particularly desirable for wooden ships where protection against weather is important. They naturally cost more to build but they are really worth while and simplify the storage problem. A well constructed box trailer serves as an excellent storage place for sailplanes.

TRAILER FOR MINIMOA
Left wing has been removed

There are many types of closed trailer in use. The simplest type uses a canvas cover over the open type trailer, it being held in place by a few posts and tie-down lugs. The simple open type can be converted into a canvas box type with the addition of the necessary framing members and canvas covering. The most durable, but heaviest, type is the wooden box where the whole trailer is completely enclosed with a covered body. A variation of this is the type that has a permanent top but removable canvas sides that permit the wings to be loaded easily. In the completely covered type the wings and fuselage have to be put in from the end, which sometimes is a lengthy and tricky job. The same protection with easier loading features is the advantage of the removable shell type. These shells of light metal framework and fabric covering fit over the trailer and completely enclose it, fastening by hooks.

The simplest and most widely used type of trailer running gear is the two-wheel type with the wheels somewhere near the center of gravity. Four-wheel trailers have been used but they are not very practical, costing more for original parts and upkeep with twice as much chance for trouble. In most cases the front axle and wheels of a light automobile work best for the running gear. If the total load is to be light, or if a heavier type of front end is to be used, some of the leaves of the springs should be removed so that it will not be too stiff. Trailers have been built with no springing except that provided by the tires, but this type is very rough on the glider.

The chassis or main framework of the trailer has been made in many types and materials. The most common are the rectangular or triangular in plan form constructed of wood or steel tubing. A good grade of lumber and low priced commercial tubing are suitable for trailers. The wooden type is easiest to construct for the beginner but the steel type results in a light, efficient trailer that will last a long time and be easily adaptable to other requirements. The main feature of the chassis should be strength, to carry through the necessary loads and stiffness so that deflection of the trailer will not strain the glider. The draw bar to which the trailer hitch is attached should be securely held in place, for failure of the draw bar has resulted in many a trailer breaking away. It is an advantage to have the chassis outline enclose all parts of the glider so that it can act as bumper. If the wings are just hung on outside the frame they are very liable to damage.

The mounting of the ship on the trailer is very important. The various parts should be mounted so that no large loads will be carried through the structure due to the deflection of the trailer or to the method of suspension. In this respect it is good practice to avoid putting any loads on the structure; rather let the parts lie in place, secured by properly padded supports. All movable surfaces should be clamped together and padded out where there is any chance of wearing or chaffing. Generous use of padding will help a lot to prevent minor damage. All clamps and pins should be of the locking variety so that vibration over a long period will not loosen some important clamp.

It is important to keep the trailer reasonably light so that it will not burden the tow car. Also, the weight carried on the tow bar should not be large as it burdens the springs of the car and makes the trailer heavy to move by hand. However, if the load is too light or if the trailer is unbalanced, the hitch has a tendency to rattle and wear and uncouple itself. There are various types of hitches available but only those of sturdy design with locking devices should be used. Safety links between trailer and car, required by many states, should be installed. The trailer lighting should comply with the state regulations and be sufficient to prevent accidents from improper lighting. The use of turn signals is advisable.

For those who are unable to build their own ships, the trailer offers an excellent opportunity to exercise their ingenuity and inventiveness. There is practically no end to the variety of trailers possible and there are no strict regulations that limit one's work. Extra time spent on trailers is well repaid in trouble-free, worry-free trailing.

MAINTENANCE

Proper maintenance of equipment is an important requirement for trouble-free gliding and soaring. Here, equipment is not meant to include only gliders and sailplanes, but also instruments, tow-ropes, trailers, tow cars, etc. Of course, failure properly to maintain the flying equipment will result more likely in trouble than in neglect of any of the others, but they are also very important. Too much faith in an instrument or in the strength of the towrope can sometimes cause as much trouble as overloaded damage to the ship. Frequent inspections and maintenance checks take little time and are a good insurance against accidents from that source.

Because of the essential lightness of gliders and sailplanes, they naturally must be treated with more care than airplanes. Their lighter construction is more susceptible to damage than the more rugged structure of the airplane. Of course, this varies with the type of ship, the primaries and utilities usually being more rugged than the sailplanes. As a matter of habit and good principle, all types should be handled carefully. Lifting in the wrong places, dropping and bumping are some of the main faults of improper handling.

In assembly a definite routine should be adopted to speed it up and avoid mistakes and possible damage. In most cases it is best to take the parts from the trailer as they are needed. Having the various parts spread all around should be avoided as they are in danger of being stepped on, run over or blown away by a sudden gust of wind. A brief inspection of parts made inaccessible by assembly should be made before assembly is started. If fitting pins are not put back in place after the ship is taken down, they should be marked so that the same pin is used each time. This is especially important with taper pins because a very good fit is necessary for ease in assembly.

In assembly, moderation should be the keynote. If something does not fit do not use force or "the hammer" until you have investigated to see what is causing the difficulty. The part may have been damaged in handling or trailing, or some foreign substance might be making the tight fit. The controls should be hooked up last, for if they are hooked up too soon they may be strained by the movement of some semi-attached part.

Once set up the ship should be thoroughly inspected and conditioned for flying. The inspection is best carried out with the aid of "fill-in" cards that list the various parts to be checked. This will tend to do away with the possibility of overlooked parts in the mad rush to get the ship in the air. Conditioning for flight usually includes: checking inflation of tire, oiling of moving parts, wiping wings and fuselage, and adjusting the various instruments, parts and controls.

In disassembly the same care should be taken as with assembly. The controls should be unhooked first and pins put back in place as soon as possible to prevent losing them. If the ship has received any rough handling in the air or in landing it should be inspected for possible damage before putting back on the trailer. In loading back on the trailer, the troughs and pads should be inspected so that any foreign substances lodged there can be removed. Dust and dirt tend to act as grinding compounds and wear the finish off.

Extensive inspections should be carried out every so often, depending upon the extent and character of operations. In this inspection every part that it is possible to see without opening any fabric or plywood should be thoroughly looked over for wear, deterioration and damage. When the ship is showing signs of wear and the fabric is getting saggy and porous, it should be recovered and completely gone over. All worn parts should be repaired or replaced and the whole structure given a protective coat of varnish or the like. In metal structures this procedure is considerably simplified. For minor repairs, of all types of constructions, parts can be replaced or repaired. But with major repairs the drawings and requirements are usually necessary to insure the use of proper methods and materials. Accepted methods and aircraft materials should be used for all repair work.

The maintenance of the trailer is an important item, for trailer trouble can easily spoil a soaring day. The various supporting brackets should be inspected for damage and wear and misplaced pads. The running gear should be inspected for mechanical trouble and lubrication, and the tires checked for wear and inflation. The hitch, chassis and lighting system should be looked over to make sure that they are in good working order. The structure should receive protective paint when necessary and the canvas covers should be treated for watertightness.

Storage, although a simple problem for metal ships, is not so simple for wooden ships, for too dry or humid conditions of storage tend to weaken the glued structure. A place of average humidity and temperature is best. Gliders are easily stored in their trailers if their mountings and paddings are designed properly. However, if wings are stored out in racks, they should be placed so that there is no strain on the wings or large local loads on any small portion. One method of storing is to leave the glider assembled, but this requires a great deal of room which is not usually available. If the ship is stored for a long period it should be inspected occasionally to make sure that everything is in good order. Leaky roofs, condensation and mice sometimes are the causes of unexpected trouble in storage.

Properly maintained equipment considerably reduces the possibility of trouble. It is a comforting thing to know that your ship is in good order and ready to take its full design loads. These extra inspections do not take long and usually they can be done when things are slow: while waiting for the tow car to come or for a wind to pick up.

THE OLYMPIC SAILPLANE

According to the rules of the 1940 Olympics, planned for Finland, all pilots competing in the contest must fly the same type of sailplane. The design of this ship was selected by the F.A.I. General specifications were issued but were of such a nature that designers were allowed a great deal of latitude. Out of five ships from Germany, Italy, and Poland, the D.F.S. "Meise," of Germany, was chosen.

The most outstanding feature of the D.F.S. "Meise" is the fact that, although the performance is excellent, the main purpose of the design is to provide a ship that can be built and handled by inexperienced workmen, without the use of expensive or complicated tools. It is a high wing type, of standard plywood construction with semi-monocque fuselage and full cantilever wings and tail. There are no complicated welded fittings or parts. It can be assembled by three men in eight minutes, and disassembled in four minutes. The specifications are as follows:

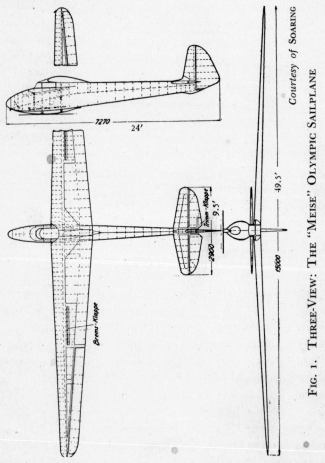

FIG. 1.   THREE-VIEW: THE "MEISE" OLYMPIC SAILPLANE

Courtesy of SOARING

Span ....49.5 sq. ft.
Wing area ....161.0 sq. ft.
Aspect ratio 15.0
Wing loading ....3.09 lbs./sq. ft.

Empty weight .... 354.0 lbs.
Gross weight .... 496.0 lbs.
Minimum sinking speed......................... 2.2 ft. per sec.
Best gliding angle .... 25 to 1
Stalling speed .... 31.5 m.p.h.

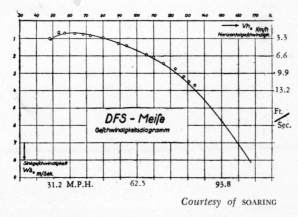

Courtesy of SOARING

FIG. 2. PERFORMANCE CURVE

Wing

The engineering of the wing was based on the wings of the D.F.S. "Reiher" and the D.F.S. "Weihe." A straight taper of 2.6 to 1 is used with an average chord of 3.3 feet. There is no gull, since it has been found by experiment that the proper combination of dihedral and rudder give sufficient stability on spiraling. The wing section varies from gö. 549 at the root (16% thickness) to gö. 676 at the tip. The 549 section extends to 60% of the semi-span. The combination of the high C_L of the tip section, and a seven degree washout at the tip, insures excellent control at the stall. A dihedral of 2.5 degrees to the neutral axis is used.

The wing is composed of a single D-spar with an I-beam web, and a very light rear spar, which carries the aileron. The aileron is hinged in four places.

The main root fittings are composed of four straps on each main spar. To simplify construction, all of them are identical. Referring to Fig. 3, the wing is attached to the fuselage by pins A, and corresponding pins in the rear spar. When pins B are removed, the wings may pivot about pins A, so that both wing tips may rest on the ground at the same time. This was done so that two people could assemble it easily. Both the wing and fuselage root fittings are attached to the structure by tubular rivets.

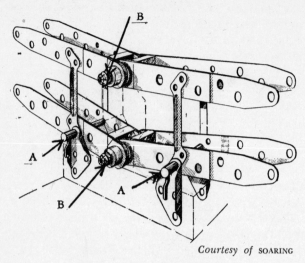

Courtesy of SOARING

FIG. 3. MAIN ROOT FITTINGS

The spoilers are shown in Fig. 4. This type of mechanism was chosen both because of its low cost and because of the ease with which it may be fitted to the wing contour. It is only necessary to make them too big and then plane off the excess material. They will not affect the wing contour by warping. It will be noted that they move in a plane parallel to the spar, and do not rotate, as is common in this country. They are enclosed in a plywood box that keeps water and dampness from entering the wing.

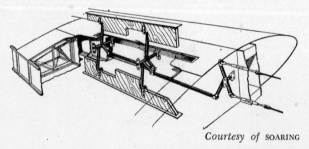

Courtesy of SOARING

FIG. 4. SPOILER MECHANISM

Fuselage

The fuselage is reinforced by bulkheads composed of two cap strips with a plywood web. They are so designed that only small strips of plywood are required, thus making it unnecessary to use up a whole sheet for each bulkhead. The cross-section behind the wing is almond shaped, for simplicity in covering and for maneuverability. For purposes of stability and sensitivity of control, the fuselage is very long (24 feet).

Following standard German practice, there is no wheel. The hardwood main skid is mounted on doughnut-shaped rubber shock absorbers, and the spring for the tail skid consists of two tennis balls.

There is a luggage and barograph compartment behind the main bulkhead, which is accessible from the outside.

Tail Surfaces

The elevator and fin are of two-spar construction with stressed skin leading edge. The spar and rib construction is identical, being a plywood web with cap strips on one side only, to form a channel section. The elevator and rudder are statically balanced, with a torsion-resistant spar and straight ribs. There is a trim tab on the elevator that can be operated in flight. The elevator and stabilizer assembly is attached to the fuselage by one bolt and wing nut.

Control System

Only four ball bearings are used in the entire control system. All other important bearings are bronze bushed and pressure lubricated. There are no press fits, and only one size of reamer is used. The control stick and torque tube installation are mounted on universal bearings so that no alignment is necessary for installation.

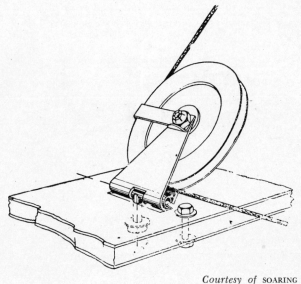

Courtesy of SOARING

FIG. 5. PULLEY INSTALLATION

All the pulleys are mounted as in Fig. 5, so that only one type of pulley and pulley bracket is necessary on the entire ship.

Either of two simple rudder pedal installations is optional. One is adjustable in flight. The other is not adjustable at any time.

The sailplane may either be built from plans furnished by the factory, or it may be bought completely built.

CHAPTER V

LAUNCHING METHODS

By Lewin B. Barringer

THE FIRST METHOD USED to launch a glider into the air was that of Lilienthal and other early pioneers who simply ran downhill into the wind until the light hang glider supported on their shoulders became air borne and in turn supported them. Since those early days a multitude of different methods has been used to launch motorless aircraft. These include: releasing from a hot-air balloon, release from a dirigible, towing behind galloping horses, towing behind an automobile, launching at the crest of a steep hill into a strong wind by having the glider pulled forward by a man at each wing, towing behind a motor boat (seaplane glider), shock-cord catapult, winch towing, and airplane towing.

Although the original method has been revived by an enthusiast in California who has built a modern version of a hang glider, and others are still occasionally used, only four of these methods have been recognized as having practical value and are now in regular use throughout the world. These, in order of their importance as well as probable use by students are: automobile towing, winch towing, shock-cord catapult, and airplane towing.

AUTO TOW

Automobile towing, proven to be the most practical and safest method for student instruction, is also useful for launching for soaring flights on large fields or on the top of ridges where there is sufficient room and a winch is not available. Equipment needed includes the automobile, release mechanism, towrope and metal rings.

The choice of a proper tow car is important; some care should be taken in acquiring one. The ideal type is a light but strongly built roadster or touring car with plenty of reserve power. The 85 h.p. Ford V-8 is an example of an excellent tow car, although many of the earlier Model A's have proven quite satisfactory and have been used extensively.

The top of the car should be down or, preferably, removed altogether so that the driver has an unobstructed view of the glider at all times. It is also best to remove the windshield, both to eliminate a possible hazard in case of accident and to allow the driver to acquire a sensitive feeling of air speed on his face which makes it unnecessary for him to watch the speedometer frequently. Although some tow cars have been rebuilt with one seat facing backward for the instructor beside the forward seat for the driver, the best method is for these two jobs to be done by one man. If the instructor is driving he can accelerate or stop the car in case of emergency more quickly than would be possible if he passed the order on to another. Also it does not take long to become so familiar with the car and the field that most of the driving can be done facing backward watching the glider.

It is sometimes advisable to have the rear of the car weighted down with 200 or 300 pounds of cast-iron weights or flat boiler plate, well secured to assure proper traction on rough ground. This can also be helped by softening up the rear springs. It is a good idea to use oversize tires at comparatively low pressure to prevent cutting up the ground if operating on a grass-covered field. If operating on soft ground or sugary sand such as is found on the Michigan beaches it is necessary to use the super-balloon tires such as were manufactured a few years ago. To get good traction even with these tires, frequently it is necessary to keep the air pressure very low.

The rear of the car must be equipped with an approved type of release either securely bolted or welded onto the framework of the car, preferably at least 2 feet off the ground. The chief purpose of this release is to enable the tow car driver immediately to detach the towrope if the release mechanism of the glider jams at the top of a tow. To operate it a light rope of about 1/4-inch diameter should lead from the trip of the release to a position within easy reach of the driver. It is usually brought over the top of the seats or around the left side of the car so that he can pull it with his left hand as he drives with his right while looking back over his left shoulder.

For primary training a 150-foot manila towrope of 3/8- or even 5/8-inch diameter should be used. Although this size of rope is too thick for greater lengths and consequently higher tows due to its high aerodynamic drag, it is better for this preliminary stage where it is subjected to much dragging on the ground which will quickly wear out lighter sizes. Five-sixteenth-diameter rope will do if the other is not available, but 1/4-inch should not be used as it is only just strong enough and will wear out very quickly.

Two other lengths of rope also should be on hand as the student

progresses; an intermediate rope of 300 feet of ⁵⁄₁₆-inch, and a
500-foot length of ¼-inch rope for high tows. The intermediate
rope can be used for perfecting 180° turns on a field or launching
off the top of a ridge. The 500-foot length is used to enable the pilot
to climb to a maximum of approximately 425 feet to make 360°
turns. On windy days or on large fields the two ropes can be joined
to make an 800-foot line enabling the pilot to get high enough to
make a much longer glide and, if the conditions are right, to encounter thermals. When such lengths are used, flags or streamers
of colored rags should be tied at intervals along the rope to make
it visible to other aircraft.

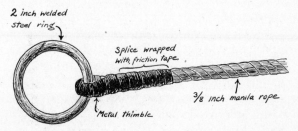

CORRECT ATTACHMENT OF RING TO END OF ROPE TOWLINE

At both ends of each of the three towlines should be fastened
welded steel rings at least 2 inches in diameter and ¼ inch in
cross-section for the average type of open releases, or the double
oval links for the DLV releases. These should be spliced on with
thimbles to prevent cutting of the rope and possible tangling of
knot ends. The splices also should be tightly wrapped with friction
tape. It is best to have the same type of release in the tow car as
on the glider to prevent possible delays in having to switch opposite ends of the rope.

A valuable scheme to speed up high tows for 360° turns, when
only the tow car driver and glider pilot are present, was developed
by the author. This scheme is as follows: have four 2-inch rings
on one 500-foot length of rope. One is fastened at each end and
the other two are fastened 40 feet in from the ends of the rope so
that these rings become links in the rope which is fastened to
them by a thimble, eye splice and tape on each side.

The tow is made as usual with one end ring in the glider release
and the other in the car release. After the glider lands the tow car
is driven to it, the driver gets out, detaches the end ring from the
car release and attaches it to the glider release. He then pulls in
40 feet of the rope and puts the second ring in the car release.
With this short length he then tows the glider back to the starting

point fast enough for the pilot to maintain lateral control, the remainder of the rope dragging behind. As the starting point is reached he slows down and maneuvers the car to turn the glider slowly around into take-off position, the down wing sliding backward on a pivoting, shock-absorbing wing skid. The driver then pulls his release, dropping the 40-foot ring, and drives off upwind along the remainder of the rope which has been automatically laid out in line by the tow back. He then jumps out, inserts the end ring in the car release, climbs back in, starts the car slowly to take up the 40 feet of slack and begins another tow. This procedure, during which the glider pilot never leaves his cockpit between flights, and the tow car driver jumps out only twice, enables a flight to 400 feet altitude to be made every 5 or 6 minutes with the glider being in the air nearly half of that time. As noted, only three of the rings actually are used on one tow back, the fourth is put in for convenience so that either end of the rope can be used.

Knots should never be allowed anywhere in a towline except, perhaps, temporarily to save time. Wear from pulling the rope along the ground will take effect much faster on a knot and will soon result in a break. All breaks should be spliced together. In making a short splice, unlay the ends of the ropes to be spliced together. The ends are crotched. In splicing a rope of moderate size the first tuck can be made by hitching together the opposing strands in the crotch, as in the first part of a reef knot. Then taper on each side. This gives one full tuck, and two tapered tucks on each side of the middle tuck.

Cast or malleable iron rings should never be used as they may crack when dropped and later fail under towing loads. Their original strength is also questionable.

Stranded metal cable and hard wire have certain advantages for towing for students that have progressed at least to the stage of making 360° turns but there are also several dangers connected with their use. The advantages are very low cost as compared to manila rope, rather long life when properly handled, and minimum aerodynamic drag. Numbers 14 and 16 soft grade spring wire are best suited for glider towing. Music wire of .056-inch diameter has proven satisfactory for lightweight gliders with a gross weight of less than 500 pounds. A bad feature of wire is kinking. Every loop may fold into a kink when the towing pull is again exerted and during the hard pull of a steep tow the wire will break. A watch should be kept for these loops and kinks by frequent inspection of the line. When they are found they should be straightened out, or if too sharp to be straightened, a cut should be made and the ends spliced together. The use of a parachute of 2- to 3-feet diameter fastened near the glider end of the wire is essential and avoids the kinks to a large extent. An old sock fastened onto the nose of the glider makes a satisfactory case for the folded parachute which is pulled out by the weight of the rope after the release. When working on hard wire with pliers or other tools care must be taken to prevent injury to the surface of the wire as this may cause a failure under load.

There is little or no resiliency to wire or cable so all the bumpings of the tow car on uneven ground are carried directly to the

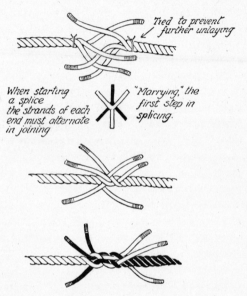

From THE SEA SCOUT MANUAL. *Courtesy of the Boy Scouts of America*

SHORT SPLICE

glider, instead of being largely absorbed by the towline as is the case when rope is used. This is apt to cause the structure of the front part of the fuselage and the wings of the glider to be unnecessarily and perhaps dangerously stressed. To prevent this a shock link is used. The simplest and cheapest consists of about 25 feet of ½- or ¾-inch rope looped and fastened onto the car end of the wire. This tends to lie out flat and therefore transmits nothing but smooth pull from the tow car to the line. It serves also as a drag when towing the line back on the ground and so tends to keep it straight. It should be formed into a loop of two strands with a ring to fit the car release. Also useful is a heavy spring of tightly coiled

¼-inch spring wire 2 inches in diameter and 18 inches to 2 feet long. Another good shock absorber can be made of a ⅝-inch shock cord. The cord should be served into an endless loop of two turns with webb straps riveted on, and provided with a ring on one end and a harness snap on the other. A disadvantage of this is that it soon will wear out from dragging over the ground. The spring and shock-cord links should both have limit cables to prevent over-loading. These should allow from 50 to 75 per cent stretch of the elastic part of the link.

All towlines, both rope and wire with the exception of the short lines used for primary training, of greater strength than ¼-inch manila rope should have a weak link provided at the glider end. This should have about the same strength as a ¼-inch manila rope and may be an 8- or 10-foot piece of that material. The purpose of this is to have the rope break before the glider becomes dangerously overstressed.

The greatest danger in the use of wire for towing is with static electricity. The glider traveling through the air acts as an excellent static accumulator, especially when constructed with metal and fabric. This may build up dangerous potentials if not conducted off to the ground continually. A continuous electrical conductor should be provided to the tow car from the glider and a metal drag chain provided from the metal structure of the car to the ground like those used on gasoline trucks for the same purpose. All gliding operations where wire or wet rope is used for towing should be sus-pended in cases of thunderstorms or any indications of other atmos-pheric conditions with heavy static nearby.

Towlines and broken ends of rope and wire are dangerous when left lying around on the field or airport. They may catch in parts of a glider or airplane and cause an accident. Towlines not in use —for even a short time—should be dragged to the edge of the field out of the way, or, better still, wound up on a simple drum turned by a hand crank.

The tow car should be operated only by an experienced driver. If gliding instructions are being given he must also be an expe-rienced pilot. The best procedure with a powerful car pulling the average glider is to start in second gear and keep in the same gear throughout the tow. This should hold true for either a short instruc-tional tow or a high tow. The chief value of staying in this gear is that the driver has better control over the towing speed due to quick acceleration or deceleration thus possible. First or low gear may be necessary to give sufficiently rapid initial acceleration to a heavy sailplane. Third or high gear may also be used on a high tow into a good breeze after the glider has reached 200 or 300 feet. If any gear changings are made while towing the glider, they must be made quickly and smoothly so as to give as little jerk as possible to the glider. To allow for the possibility of the student pulling back too steeply and overstressing the wings to the danger point the tow car driver must be careful not to tow too fast. It is a safe rule to limit this speed to 40 m.p.h. in still air and proportionately less if a wind is blowing.

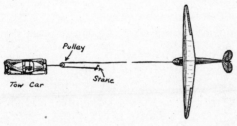

AUTO-PULLEY LAUNCHING

To give quick acceleration on ridge top launching fields of limited area as well as to save wear and tear on tow cars running over rough ground, a system using a pulley has been developed to a high degree of efficiency in California. First used at the Torrey Pines Mesa site north of San Diego this system uses one pulley of 6 to 10 inches diameter with oversize flanges attached to the car by a 6-inch length of rope. One end of a ⅜-inch rope is attached to a low stake driven firmly into the ground. It is then brought around the pulley and the other end, equipped with a ring, is attached to the glider release. The car is driven into the wind at half the flying speed of the glider.

There is, however, a serious drawback to this auto-pulley-tow system, and that is the impossibility of releasing the rope at the towing end in the event of failure of the glider release mechanism. One way to avoid this risk would be to have someone with a sharp knife or, preferably, a pair of sharp shears, standing near the stake.

In starting a tow the driver must be careful to drive the car very slowly until the slack has been taken up entirely before using full power to accelerate as quickly as possible. When a long rope is used and a third person is at hand to hold the wing tip it is customary for him to leave the wing tip down until the slack is out; then, to show that the slack is out and also that the glider pilot is ready to take off, he holds the wing level. When no third person is present the pilot can kick his rudder full from one side to the other as a signal to the driver.

The tow car driver must realize that his is a serious responsibility. He must be keen and alert at all times. Before a tow he must make sure that the car is filled with gas, oil and water, the tires held at proper pressure, the steering mechanism tight and oiled, and the engine running smoothly and warmed up. He must also make sure that the field and air are clear. During the tow he must be constantly on the alert to prevent towing too fast or too slowly and must always be ready to stop the car or release the towline in case of an emergency.

WINCH TOW

During the past few years winch towing as a means of launching gliders has rapidly grown in favor until it is now recognized as the most efficient method for pilots past the "B" license or 360° turn stage. With this system an engine-driven drum winds up the rope and replaces the towing automobile to accelerate the glider to flying speed. Two of its advantages are very quick acceleration and perfectly smooth towing. Another is the fact that only the glider and the drum are accelerated, which puts considerably less load on the engine as compared to auto tow where the whole car has to be brought up to the flying speed of the glider. Sometimes, also, higher tows can be made than are usually possible by auto tow because the towrope or wire can be laid across rough ground unsuitable for the tow car.

Given a smooth field as a launching area the maximum height possible is approximately the same for winch as for auto tow. Using 3500 feet of towline on a runway the same length with a 5-10 m.p.h. wind the average glider can be climbed to about 800 feet before having to be released. The same height can be reached by auto tow with a 1000-foot length of towline, the car traveling 2500 feet.

A variety of winches has been built by different glider clubs. Most have been successful and many have incorporated new and useful devices. However, no standard type has yet been built with all the good features of these winches so the best of them will be described. Probably the first successful glider launching winch in America was that built by Gustave Scheurer at Millington, New Jersey. It was also the simplest design and the forerunner of many built since.

Using a Model T Ford as motive power, a drum was bolted to the right rear wheel. That wheel was jacked up and the other wheels were blocked. Towing was done in high gear and the towline was wound on smoothly by being guided with two sticks held by someone standing beside the car. Shortly afterwards the Y Flying

Club of Newark, New Jersey, built a similar winch on a 1919 Dodge sedan using a 16-inch diameter drum with flanges made of 1/4-inch metal plates bringing the outside diameter to 30 inches. Wooden pulleys, mounted on bicycle front wheel hubs, were used for guide rollers. The side rollers were steel tubes mounted on Ford generator bearings. This design was later improved by changing the drum to the left rear wheel with the rope feeding through a second set of guide rollers on the left front fender. The first set of rollers was mounted on a level winding, hand-operated device placed just behind the driver's seat so that he could operate it when a second person was not present. The principal objection to a winch with drum mounted on the rear wheel of a car is that the unusual load exerted on the wheel bearing on that side due to the differential of the rear axle is apt soon to wear out the bearings.

THE SCHEURER WINCH ON MODEL T FORD IN 1928

The main essentials of a glider winch are an engine-driven drum which will hold 4000 to 6000 feet of $\frac{5}{16}$-inch manila rope, a level winding device, guide rollers, a rope cut-off device, and a brake to stop the drum. This should be of such diameter that towline speeds up to 45 m.p.h. are possible without excessive engine speeds.

The ideal level winding device is one automatically operated by a worm gear connected to the driving mechanism. With such a device properly geared one can be sure of smooth winding of the towline without having to pay any attention to it. To save cost, however, most winches have been built with a manually-operated winding device. One of the best examples of this is the system used on the Meeker winch built in Detroit. With this compact unit, evolved from a Model A Ford, and moved about as a trailer, the operator turns the erstwhile steering wheel of the car to turn the winding device as he sits facing away from the engine and toward the glider being towed. Although it gives the winch operator more to do and think about, this type of manual winder is preferable to the hand type which is more generally used and requires another man to operate it.

Another interesting solution of a one-man winch using a manual winder is that built by the Purdue Glider Club. In this winch the drum is mounted directly on the drive shaft of a Model A chassis. The drive shaft has been discontinued from turning the rear wheels, so this winch must also be moved by towing as a trailer. A throttle has been mounted within easy reach of the operator who stands beside the drum where he can shift gears, use the brake and push back and forth the level winder equipped with guide rollers.

If possible the guide rollers should be at least 4 inches in diameter to avoid excessive rotational speeds. They should be made of steel rather than bronze so that a wire towline also can be used. Wire will soon cut grooves into bronze rollers. The chief advantage of using wire on a winch instead of rope is when operations are being carried out on beaches where there is loose, wet sand. Wet rope soon picks up enough sand to more than double its weight, making high tows impracticable. The sand also has a very destructive effect on the winch bearings which are exposed to it. Another advantage, which is sometimes more than outweighed by the troubles of kinking and frequent breakage is that higher tows are possible due to the minimum aerodynamic drag. Tests with a sailplane of 700 pounds gross weight on a 4000-foot field in a 15-20-mile wind and a climbing airspeed of 42 m.p.h. resulted in a maximum altitude before release of 1500 feet using a wire towline. This was approximately 300 feet higher than possible with ⅜-inch manila rope.

The rope cut-off device, usually called the guillotine, is essential for safe towing operations which must always allow for a means of detaching the towline at the towing end in case of a failure of the glider release. Mechanical failures of approved type of releases have been very rare, but there have also been human failures where the pilots forgot to release and were saved from serious and perhaps fatal accidents because the winch operator was able to cut the rope. Lacking such a device some gliding clubs have a man standing near the drum with a hatchet. For wire towing large pliers have replaced the hatchet. Quick twists in opposite directions will easily snap wire. However, these are no better than makeshifts and can never replace a well-designed guillotine for quick, sure severing of the towline.

Fred T. Loomis

THE DU PONT WINCH LAUNCHES THE "ALBATROSS" AT ELMIRA

One type of guillotine uses a single knife blade held up horizontally against the pull of two strong springs by a simple trigger device. When the operator pulls the string attached to the trigger, the blade is pulled down by the springs against a solid metal block against which the towline is cut. Another excellent guillotine was that developed by E. Paul du Pont on his winch. This consisted of two blades mounted behind the guide rollers. Strong rubber bands acted as springs, the blades being mounted in such a position that their leverage was powerful enough, when tripped, to snap a broom handle placed between them. This winch was later changed and the guillotine made like the French executioner's machine in having the knife made very heavy and its weight, when released,

BROWN-WOODRUFF WINCH

Incorporating independent power unit, automatic level winder, guillotine, and operator's seat facing to rear.

being accelerated downward by heavy rubber bands giving the same cutting power as the first type. With a cutting device of such power there is real danger of serious injury for the careless and inquisitive onlookers; prominent signs should be placed to warn them away when the winch is ready to tow. When not in operation the knife should be left down or blocked so that it cannot be tripped accidentally.

A brake for the drum of a winch is absolutely necessary. In most winches acquiring their power from the rear wheels of a car this essential is supplied by the foot brake of the car. In winches like the Brown-Woodruff where a separate power unit drives the winch a shoe brake is mounted on a small drum on the axle of the winch drum.

THE M. I. T. WINCH

One of the most successful winches developed in recent years is the one built by the Aeronautical Engineering Society of Massachusetts Institute of Technology in Cambridge under the direction of Parker Leonard and Karl Lange. A La Salle sedan was stripped to the chassis as far forward as the driver's seat. The drum was mounted over the rear wheels and actuated by friction from both rear wheels through a second set of wheels and tires mounted at either end of the drum shaft. When operating built-in jacks raise the rear wheels clear of the ground. When the winch is being driven cross country the drum and its wheels are jacked up away from them. An automatic level winding device is built above the drum and the towline runs forward through a second set of guide rollers mounted above the windshield. The operator faces in the direction of the glider and can use the throttle, clutch, gear shift and brake of the car to control the winch. A copy of this winch was built on an Auburn sedan chassis by the Airhoppers Gliding and Soaring Club on Long Island.

The same rules about towlines as described under AUTO TOW hold true for winch towing, with the one exception, of course, that length of towline unwound from the drum is determined only by the extent of the operating field. A weak link of about 600 pounds strength (¼-inch rope) should be used ahead of the shock link on the glider end when using wire. The parachute is also necessary. When using rope no knots of any kind should be permitted. End connections can be made by a short splice of not less than 6 tucks. Eye connections to rings should be protected with thimbles and eye splices made with at least 3 tucks.

The operation of a winch requires more skill than tow car driving and should be done only by or under the close supervision of someone thoroughly familiar with it. The tow must be started in the gear to be used throughout the tow as the drum does not have enough inertia to permit gear shifting without danger of fouling the line. The choice of gear to be used depends on the power and pick-up of the engine, the gear ratio of the engine to the drum, the weight and drag of the glider and the wind velocity.

A set of flag signals should be used in winch towing and these should be thoroughly understood by everyone taking a part in the launching. A good scheme is to use red and white flags about 3 feet square on light sticks or poles 6 feet long. Some clubs use a red flag mounted on the winch or stuck in the ground near the glider, denoting that things are not yet ready at that end of the line. When the winch operator is ready to tow he substitutes the white flag for the red. When the glider pilot has fastened his safety belt, closed his cockpit cover and is ready to be launched, he calls to the man holding his wing tip. This helper then holds the wing tip level and either he with his other hand, or someone else if available, holds the white flag over his head and waves it slowly from side to side. This is the signal to take up slack which may have to be repeated by a second signal man halfway to the winch if the tow is very long or over a slight elevation.

The winch driver, having previously given his ready signal denoting that the winch engine is running and has been warmed up, lets out his clutch slowly to take up the slack gradually. When the ship begins to move the signal man at the glider drops his flag and the winch operator gives the engine full throttle to accelerate the drum as quickly as possible to the proper towing speed for the wind velocity at the time. It is helpful to have a wind sock or wind velocity device of some kind such as an anemometer mounted on the winch so that the operator may keep posted on the wind direction and velocity at all times.

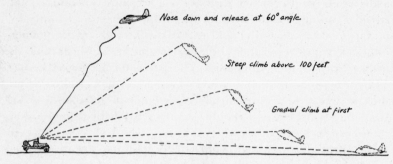

Nose down and release at 60° angle

Steep climb above 100 feet

Gradual climb at first

WINCH LAUNCHING

A pilot experienced in winch towing takes off in a gradual climb until he is about 100 feet high. This is to allow the winch operator to get the drum up to the speed where the engine will have enough power to handle the climb as well as to prevent the danger of a stall resulting from towline breakage too low to recover. Above this height he may pull back quite steeply to get the maximum height possible from the tow which is much smoother than auto tow, permitting a steeper climb without undue strain on the glider. As the glider changes to the steeper climb the winch should be slowed down to keep the glider air speed at the correct velocity. Too fast a tow will prevent a maximum climb and will overload the wings of the glider. The final speed near the end of the tow usually will be about one half the maximum unless the wind velocity tends to increase with altitude, in which case it may be less.

The pilot should watch his airspeed indicator closely and may use an arm signal to indicate to the winch operator whether he is being towed too slowly or too fast. Sudden variations in the angle of climb should be avoided as it is difficult to vary the towline velocity to allow for these changes. Drifting off to the side should also be avoided. If the wind has changed direction slightly so that the tow is crosswind the glider can be kept in a straight line toward the winch by a slight crabbing accomplished by holding a certain amount of rudder in the direction of the wind.

As in auto tow, the pilot should level out before releasing the towline. If he waits too long before releasing he may start to be accelerated downward which will give him a false feeling of excessive flying speed when in fact the glider may actually be stalled. A turn made under this condition is likely to result in a spin.

The winch operator should avoid this by gradually slowing up the drum as the towline reaches this angle. If the glider pilot hangs on a bit too long the winch operator should bring the drum to a full stop. If he still does not release after this the operator should trip the guillotine and cut the towline.

The moment the pilot releases the towline the winch operator must throw out the clutch and pull on the brake. Retrieving the towline for the next launching is usually done by towing it back with a car while the winch clutch is out. The car should be driven back at a very even speed of not faster than 10-15 m.p.h. as otherwise the towline may backlash and be damaged, causing failures under strain. The winch operator must be ready to apply the brake on the drum as the car stops. It is usually well to drive about 10 feet past the glider before dropping the end of the towline if it is rope, due to its elasticity which may make it pull back. The retrieving car should be slowed down gradually and brought to a full stop before dropping the rope.

Rope towline should never be left on the drum after the last tow but should be unwound completely from the drum after the tow and rewound without tension. It should be protected from rain and dew which will tend to shrink it. It should be inspected frequently for weak spots, and these cut and spliced.

SHOCK-CORD LAUNCHING

Launching by means of a rubber-rope or shock-cord catapult is not nearly so frequently used now as formerly. However, it still remains as the only means of launching for slope soaring from the top of ridges where the take-off areas are too limited for auto or winch tow methods. There are two types of shock-cord launchings. In the first the elastic rope is stretched by man power, and in the second by an automobile.

The shock cord is a 5/8-inch diameter bundle of elastic rubber bands which have been stretched and covered with a loosely woven binding keeping the strands stretched about 100% of their natural length. This cord requires about 375 pounds' pull per strand to double its length when new. For gliders of less than 400 pounds gross weight two strands of about 100 feet long are used. For heavier ships a double cord (four strands) is used.

For a safety measure, about 35 feet of 1/2-inch manila rope should be served into the vertex of a shock-cord V so as to isolate the glider and pilot in case of cord failure. A welded steel ring of at least 2-inch diameter is fastened to the end of this rope by means of thimble and eye splice thoroughly taped. When ready to launch this ring is slipped over the open hook located on the nose of the glider below and behind the closed hook release mechanism used for the other types of launching. Its action is automatic, the ring dropping free as the glider overtakes the shock cord and the slack comes in the cord at the end of the pull.

The cord eye should be served with a galvanized iron thimble to prevent a sharp bend in the cord. The whole joint should be protected from abrasive wear by a covering of friction tape. The two loose ends should have about 30 feet of ½-inch rope served onto each if the cord is to be used for auto-tow shock-cord launching.

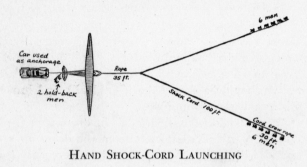

HAND SHOCK-CORD LAUNCHING

Hand shock-cord launching requires a set-up which varies with the contour of the take-off area. When this is level and flat over the whole area, the cord is laid out in V form so that the glider wing tips will just clear the cord crew. In this type of launching it is necessary to store up enough energy in the cord by stretching it by the crew so that upon release of the tail anchorage of the glider it will be catapulted to a velocity somewhat above flying speed before the end of the take-off area is reached by the cord crew. It is important to be careful not to set the glider so far back from the edge of the hill that it will get dangerously low before it reaches the area of lift. The set-up must be kept as far out toward the edge of the slope as possible and still have room for an effective launching. In the case where the take-off area is sloping ground and the glider is sure to go above the crew, the two lines may be brought in so that they are within 10 or 15 feet of each other. Four to seven men may be used on each strand of cord.

The tail of the glider should be provided with a ring or hook for the hold-back rope. One of the best ways to anchor the glider while the shock cord is being stretched is to have one end of the rope tied to a car or trailer of sufficient weight, the rope slipped through the ring or hook on the tail and have one or two men sitting on the ground holding the other end.

The glider pilot gives the commands for the shock-cord launching. After he is seated in the glider with safety belt fastened and ready to take off he first makes sure that a man is holding his wing tip level, the tail is anchored by the hold-back crew and the shock-cord crew are at their posts holding the cord. He then gives the order "WALK" and the cord crew walks forward about 12 paces, after which he gives the order "RUN." When the crew has run about the same number of paces, having pulled the cord to about 80% to 90% of its possible stretch, the pilot calls "LET GO." The tail crew simply drops the rope and the glider shoots forward. The cord crew continues to run until the glider passes over them and the cord drops free.

Elmira Star Gazette

SHOCK-CORD LAUNCHING OF FRANKLIN UTILITY GLIDER

The acceleration is so fast that the pilot has no time to think before he is well out over the side of the mountain. He should therefore be sure to hold his stick at neutral or even a little farther forward to keep the glider from zooming upward. He should try to fly straight ahead with no more than a slight climb of a few feet. The tremendous energy of the catapult launching is short lived and he may waste it if he pulls up too sharply. Also he may have to fly ahead some distance into a strong head wind before reaching the area of lift beyond the edge of the ridge.

As this very sudden acceleration in shock-cord launching is apt to be more than a little disconcerting for a new pilot who has never done it, no student should be launched from a hilltop until he has had practice on a level field. It is also wise for any pilot no matter how experienced to try out a shock-cord launching on a level field before attempting a launching in a sailplane new to him and from a site not yet tested by others who are present to advise him.

Auto shock-cord launching is very similar with the automobile taking the place of the cord crew. Flag signals are used instead of verbal commands. The lines connected to the ends of the cord are brought together and fastened to the release on the tow car. A point on the ground is marked for about 50% stretch of the cord so that the driver can signal for the tail release when the car has passed that point. This signal is passed on by the wing tip man to the tail crew. Less stretch is needed than for hand launching as the mass and speed of the car are both greater than with hand pull.

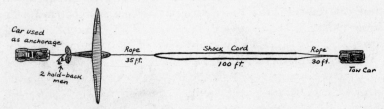

AUTO SHOCK-CORD LAUNCHING

Low gear should be used throughout the tow. The driver should decide beforehand after consultation with the pilot in which direction he will turn in case there is any possible danger of the glider not clearing the car. There is also danger for the tow car driver in case of too abrupt a turn at the end of the launching on a downslope. The forces involved in auto shock-cord launching are much higher than in straight auto tow, so the car release and its attachment should have ample strength for this work.

There is a real element of danger in shock-cord launchings in the event of the failure of any of the equipment used. If any of the ropes, metal rings, or the cord itself should break under the terrific strain before the glider is released it may result in serious injury. If the break occurs at the crew or car end the force may be sufficient to smash the nose of the glider and injure the pilot. If a failure happens at the glider end a cord crew member or the tow car driver may be injured. For this reason it is essential to use the best of materials and to keep them in good condition. The cord should be inspected frequently for any indication of wear or failure either of the cord itself or of its fastenings. When not in use it should be stored in a cool, dark and dry place.

AIRPLANE TOW

Contrary to common belief, airplane towing of gliders as a means of launching is not hazardous if carried out according to proper rules of proven procedure. Unless the air is unusually turbulent the stresses on the glider in towed flight are actually substantially less than in other methods of launching.

To do airplane towing in the United States one must have a glider that has been licensed for this type of operation. This license usually requires that the glider be placarded for the maximum allowable speeds in towed flight. It is essential therefore that both the airplane and the glider be equipped with airspeed indicators. It is also required by the Civil Air Regulations that both pilots wear parachutes. The airplane pilot must hold a Commercial Pilot's Certificate and the glider pilot must have a Commercial Glider Pilot's Certificate as well as a Certificate of Non-Application to the C.A.R. ruling that no aircraft be towed behind another aircraft except by special permission of the Civil Aeronautics Authority.

Primary gliders can never be airplane towed as they lack sufficient strength, stability and protection. Towing is usually done in well designed secondary or utility gliders and intermediate and high performance sailplanes.

The ideal towing airplane is an open cockpit biplane with light wing loading of less than 8 pounds per square foot and consequently low stalling speed, and between 90 and 220 h.p. Light airplanes of 40 h.p. have been used from large fields but they lack sufficient reserve power and the required full rearward visibility. As the best average towing speed is 50-55 m.p.h., the airplane should have a stalling speed of not over 45 m.p.h. and preferably less. Excellent American tow planes are the Waco F and the Fleet biplanes with Warner or Kinner engines of from 100 to 145 h.p.

The airplane should be equipped with an approved release device similar to that used in the glider. Complicated and costly towing attachments transmitting the towing forces over the tail surfaces and directly to the center of gravity of the airplane have been used abroad but the American system of attaching the release directly to the tail skid or tail wheel of the airplane has proven more practical in every way. The slipstream tends to lay out the first part of the towline directly behind the airplane regardless of the angle the glider may be pulling on it so no trouble need be expected from the towline fouling the rudder or elevators. The rope or cable tripping the release can be run inside the fuselage to the pilot's cockpit in a permanent installation or around the outside for the usual temporary arrangement.

The towline should be ¼-inch manila rope at least 300 feet long and equipped with metal rings at each end just like the towline for auto towing. For cross-country towing or student instruction it is advisable to use a 400-foot towline if the size of the field will permit it. On the average field at sea level and in quiet air the take-off run of the airplane will be increased from 200 to 300 feet. Using a cable instead of a rope towline will reduce the drag on the airplane, but it must be supplemented with a 20-foot length of ¼-inch rope, preferably at the airplane end, to give some elasticity and to provide a weak link.

Before starting a tow the pilots of the airplane and the glider should talk over all details of the tow and thoroughly understand their signals if any are to be used. *Under no circumstances should an airplane tow be made with both pilots inexperienced in this type of towing.* A tow may be made with a capable airplane pilot who has never towed a glider before if the glider pilot is experienced in airplane towing. Also a safe tow may be made with the airplane pilot experienced in airplane towing and the glider pilot new to this type of launching if he has had complete verbal instructions.

After the glider is thoroughly inspected it should be set at the end of the field to permit the longest tow as nearly into the wind as possible. The towline should then be laid out straight and the other ring attached to the airplane. After checking both releases by tripping them with the line under tension, the airplane should be warmed up. When ready it should move slowly ahead to take up the slack in the line. If the pilot should run up his engine at the last moment he should throttle back and wait a moment until the air has quieted down before starting a tow.

When ready the glider pilot calls to the man holding his wing tip level, who gives a hand or flag signal to the airplane pilot. In starting, the airplane pilot should simply make a normal take-off. The only difference he may notice is that his tail may come up more slowly than usual to flying position and that his ground run is somewhat longer. Once in the air he should watch his airspeed indicator closely, keeping a constant speed not exceeding that allowed by the placard on the glider. He should make gradual turns. If the air is turbulent he must fly as slowly as possible, consistent with safety. If he is the gliding instructor of the glider pilot he may use hand signals or rock his wings gently from side to side indicating to the student when to release. As soon as he sees that the glider is off he throttles back and dives down to get the rope away from the glider. The best way for him to drop it on the field is to dive down at 70-80 m.p.h. with engine partly throttled so that the line will string out and up away from obstructions and then pull the release when he is about 200-300 feet in the air over the center of the field. All towing of beginners should be made in quiet air.

As he begins to move forward on the take-off the glider pilot holds his stick at neutral. As he reaches flying speed he should pull back gently and climb to about 15-20 feet. Then he should dive down to about half that height to allow the rope to slacken a bit and the airplane to take off. During the climb and throughout the tow he should fly directly behind the airplane and perhaps also 5-10 feet above its line of flight. If he drops well below he is in danger of getting into the slipstream which, with all American engines rotating clockwise, is spiraling off down and to the left. If this happens his left wing may drop and he may have trouble bringing it up again. If he cannot soon lift it back level he must release.

If the glider pilot should pull up too high on the take-off before the airplane leaves the ground he may lift the tail of the airplane and cause the propeller to hit the ground and be damaged. Pulling

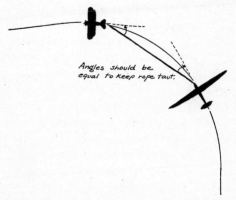

A Correct Turn in Airplane Towing

up too high when the airplane is flying at low altitude is even more dangerous as the plane can be put into a dive from which the pilot cannot recover in time before crashing into the ground. In a well executed airplane tow the glider pilot flies formation with the airplane closely watching the glider's every movement and trying at all times to stay in the same position with respect to it. This may seem somewhat difficult at first but becomes easy with practice.

In making a turn in towed flight the glider should be steered toward the outside of the circle to keep the towline taut. If the airplane is making a right turn the glider pilot holds enough left rudder to accomplish this. The airplane must maintain power at all times while towing. If it is necessary to lose altitude in tow this must also be done with power on and gradually to prevent excessive speed which will cause the glider to overtake the airplane.

Special care must be taken when towing on days of good convection when there are strong up and down currents. If the airplane encounters an upcurrent it may be lifted well above the glider which then runs into danger of getting into the slipstream. When the glider pilot sees the airplane rising suddenly above him he should immediately pull back and attempt to stay behind it. This is usually not hard as at towing speed it has plenty of reserve speed for this.

If the glider is in an upcurrent when the airplane is not it will be quickly lifted high above or will catch up with the airplane if the pilot is not careful. A valuable way to lose height to stay behind the airplane is to open the spoilers increasing drag and reducing lift. The glider can also be skidded from side to side to slow it up and take the slack out of the rope.

Both pilots should be prepared to release immediately in case of emergency. If the airplane pilot should experience engine failure on the take-off he must release the line at once. The glider pilot must be ready to do the same right afterwards, as attempting to land with the line dragging may cause it to snag in trees or other obstructions. The glider pilot may suddenly find himself in a violent upcurrent of such turbulence that his craft is becoming dangerously stressed and in this case he should release. Usually he is given warning of approaching conditions as he sees the airplane encounter them first. No towing should be done in a glider that is incorrectly rigged so that there is wing heaviness on one side. If a pilot should find himself being towed in a glider in this condition he should cut loose as soon as he is high enough so that the towline trailing behind the airplane will not foul in anything on the ground, and to enable himself to make a safe landing.

CHAPTER VI

SOARING METEOROLOGY

By Dr. Karl O. Lange

THE POWER REQUIRED for soaring is not derived from any power plant carried by the craft, but has to be taken directly from the energies available in the atmosphere. At our present state of experience, the atmospheric energy is used extensively only in the form of upcurrents. These upcurrents are wind currents which have an upward component.

Soaring meteorology is chiefly concerned with the study of upcurrents of a size that can be utilized in flight. It points out the possibilities and dangers of the atmosphere as a source of energy. A fundamental knowledge of these meteorological facts is required of any glider pilot who hopes to be successful.

Glider pilots differentiate among several frequently encountered kinds of upcurrents in the atmosphere:

1. Dry thermals
2. Slope winds
3. Cumulus clouds, including heat thunderstorms
4. Cloud streets and waves
5. Squalls and fronts, including front thunderstorms
6. The "Moazagotl" condition

To understand them, it is necessary first to get acquainted with some general characteristics of the lower atmosphere.

The Temperature of the Atmosphere

The temperature of the earth and the atmosphere are the result of radiation received from the sun and radiation sent out from the earth into space. The amount of sun's radiation received at a particular location depends on the position of the sun; in other words, on the latitude, the season, and the time of day.

The sun's rays enter the earth's region at the outer atmosphere. If the atmosphere is clear, they penetrate the transparent medium without losing more than 20 or 30% of their energy until they hit the earth's surface. Here, they are partly reflected but mostly absorbed and converted into heat, thus making the temperature rise.

If the sky, however, contains clouds or haze, then a certain percentage of the sun's radiation is reflected, dispersed, and absorbed during its passage through the atmosphere, and only the remaining part can heat the earth's surface. Thus the diurnal rise of temperature on the ground is less pronounced on such days.

The earth's radiation into space takes place all the time. It tends to lower the surface temperature, and is particularly noticeable by this effect at night when not compensated by solar radiation.

The intensity of radiation depends on many factors, notably on the temperature. The energy sent out from any body is proportional to the fourth power of the absolute temperature T

$$E = \text{const.} \times T^4$$

The absolute temperature is $273 + t$, where t is the surface temperature in Centigrade. For example, if the ground temperature of a certain location is 100° F., more than twice as much heat is radiated off as when the ground is only 10° F.

On clear nights this radiation leaves the earth and little returns from the atmosphere, causing the temperature to drop. "Clear cold" nights are proverbial. However, if the sky is covered with a cloud layer or if there is fog or haze, large amounts of the earth's radiation are reflected back and absorbed. Consequently the night does not become so cold as it would have had it been clear. We see that clouds or fog or even haze again tend to diminish the diurnal change of temperature on the ground.

These considerations show that the character of the sky plays a role in determining the temperature on the earth. They show too that the temperatures of the atmosphere are to some degree directly affected by radiation. The warming up process during the day starts and is most pronounced at the ground. The same is the case with cooling at night. More often than not, a diurnal temperature variation of 20° at the ground is diminished to nothing at the 6000 foot level.

Generally speaking, we find the highest temperatures at the earth's surface. From there, heat is transferred into the higher layers of the atmosphere partly by conduction, but mostly by a turbulent exchange of air, and by condensation processes. The result is that ordinarily the temperature decreases rapidly with altitude. The rate at which the temperature drops depends on many factors, notably the time of day and the season and the location on the earth's surface at which the air mass is found or over which it had originally formed and traveled. The actual temperature conditions in the atmosphere show great variations, but as a first approximation and for many purposes the temperature can be considered to fall off on the average at a rate of 3° F. per 1000 feet.

The rate at which the temperature changes with altitude is called the temperature lapse rate. The atmosphere is said to be stable or to have a stable lapse rate if the rate of change is less than 5.5° F. per 1000 feet. If it is 6° F. or more per 1000 feet, the atmosphere is called unstable. If the temperature does not change vertically, the condition is called isothermal, and if the temperature increases with altitude, we have an inversion. If such a layer in which the temperature increases with altitude starts right at the earth's surface, it is called a ground inversion. The lapse rate is usually represented by a curve in a diagram where temperatures are the abscissae and where altitudes (or logarithms of air pressure) are the ordinates. Fig. 1 depicts the various possible lapse rates in the atmosphere.

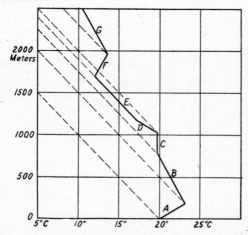

FIG. 1. TEMPERATURE LAPSE RATES IN THE ATMOSPHERE

A = ground inversion, B = stable lapse rate, C = isothermal condition, D = superadiabatic lapse rate, E = adiabatic lapse rate, F = inversion, G = stable lapse rate. The dotted lines represent adiabatic changes of state as they occur in "dry thermals."

The vertical temperature distribution in the atmosphere is not only important for soaring, but is connected with many other weather phenomena. For this reason, the daily determination of these conditions all over the country now forms an important part of the routine weather observations. The U. S. Government determines the atmospheric temperatures early every morning at more than thirty points scattered all over the United States by means of radio-meteorgraph (radiosonde) ascensions. These measurements are made and used in the metric system. The temperature is expressed in Centigrade, the altitude in meters, and the pressure in millibars. Five Centigrade degrees is equal to 9 Fahrenheit degrees, and 0° C. corresponds to the freezing point, 32° F. One hundred meters is approximately 330 feet; 1000 millibars is equivalent to 29.5 inches of mercury. These radiosonde ascensions are now undoubtedly the most valuable material for the determination and forecasting of soaring conditions. When used with due consideration of the diurnal changes which take place in the lower layers, the soundings give a true picture of the energies available for soaring, as is shown in the following pages.

The Air Pressure

The air pressure is the result of the weight of the atmospheric gases. (On a winter day, a cubic meter of air at the surface weighs almost 3 pounds.) Naturally, the air pressure is always highest at the ground, because the entire atmosphere lies on top. At a higher elevation, part of the air is left underneath, and only the air on top exerts its weight. Consequently the air pressure decreases with altitude.

The rate at which the air pressure decreases with height depends on the density of the air. The density in turn depends on air pressure, air temperature, and moisture content. Since these factors vary from day to day and from location to location and from height to height, the exact rate of pressure change with height must vary too. In order to obtain accurate correlation of pressure and height, it is necessary first to measure all temperatures, humidities, and pressures from the ground up. Thus all air densities from the ground up can be determined. By integration, it is then possible to compute the pressures which are found at certain altitudes. These computations are carried out every day at the radiosonde stations and the results may be obtained from the U. S. Weather Bureau, if needed for the exact determination of altitudes from barographs or for check-up on altimeters. If a smaller degree of accuracy is sufficient, the data may be taken from tables which are computed for the "standard atmosphere." The standard atmosphere assumes a constant temperature and a constant pressure on the ground, and a constant, stable lapse rate of 3.57° F. per 1000 ft.

Air Density and Lift

The density of ideal gases is given by temperature and pressure. The air consists of a mixture of nitrogen, oxygen, carbon dioxide, water vapor, and small quantities of other gases. All except the water vapor behave as ideal gases under ordinary atmospheric conditions. Therefore, when neglecting the presence of water vapor in the atmosphere for the present, we can say that the air follows the gas laws. The density of dry air is

$$\varrho = 1.18 \frac{p}{T}$$

where ϱ = density in kg per cubic meter
p = pressure in inches of mercury
T = absolute temperature.

For example, at a pressure of 30 inches and a temperature of 32° F., the air density is 1.293 kg per cubic meter. At the same pressure, but at a temperature of 86° F., it would be only 1.178 kg, more than 10% lighter.

If a body is submerged in a liquid, it receives a lift which is equal to the weight of the liquid which it replaces. The weight of the body acts contrary to this lift. Consequently, if the density of the body is higher than that of the liquid, it sinks. If the body is lighter than the liquid, it receives a free lift. The lifting force is proportional to the density difference.

This law holds for gases as it does for liquids, as demonstrated by airships and balloons. That means that a quantity of air contained in air of a higher density receives a free lift, and it holds true whether the quantity of air is held together in a hot air balloon or is just an air bubble, the temperature of which is higher than the surroundings.

So long as the air is not contained in a closed balloon, like a rubber toy balloon, the air pressure inside and outside will always be equal. Thus the density difference, which determines the free lift, can simply be expressed in terms of temperature. The upward acceleration created on a quantity of air of a temperature T, submerged in the atmosphere of a temperature T_0 is

$$b = g \frac{T - T_0}{T_0}$$

g is the gravity constant
T is expressed in absolute degrees

For example, if on a summer day with a temperature of 300° (81° F.), a quantity of air blows slowly over a particularly hot spot on the ground, getting heated up to 301° (83° F.), it would experience an upward acceleration of 3.2 cm./sec./sec. This is not much, only about one third of a per cent of the gravity acceleration. However, if the temperature difference were maintained long enough, as the "thermal" moves upward, the upcurrent would soon be accelerated to appreciable vertical velocities. If the thermal rises under a steady acceleration b its vertical speed V_z at a height H would be $V_z = \sqrt{2bH}$

Friction between the upcurrent and the undisturbed atmosphere reduces the speed by 20% to 30%, so that

$$V_z = 0.75 \times \sqrt{2bH}$$

For example, at a height of 100 feet, the upcurrent would be about 1 meter per second. At 1000 feet it would have grown to about 3.3 meters per second.

These considerations show that there are two requirements for strong thermal currents. Either the temperature difference must be very large, which is seldom experienced, or the temperature difference between thermal and surroundings must be maintained over a considerable range of altitude to permit building up of high vertical speeds.

The Temperature Variation of an Ascending Current

If a gas expands from one pressure to a lower one, its molecules have to be distributed over a wider space. The energy required to do this is taken out of the gas in the form of heat, thus lowering the temperature of the gas. Similarly, when a gas is compressed, its temperature rises.

A quantity of air which moves upward in the atmosphere comes under lower pressure. That is, it expands and its temperature drops. If the current moves downward, the opposite takes place. The air temperature rises. Provided that no heat is added or subtracted during the process of vertical movement, then the temperature of the vertical current changes almost exactly 1° C. per 100 meters. Such a process, in which no exchange of heat with the surroundings or by radiation takes place, is called an adiabatic process. And a lapse rate of 1° C. per 100 meters is therefore called an adiabatic lapse rate.

All slope currents and all "dry thermals" follow this law. There is naturally a certain amount of turbulent mixing along the edges of the upcurrents, which tends to establish a gradual change from the temperatures of the current to those of the surroundings. The inside of the vertical current, however, changes 1° C. per 100 meters (approximately 5.5° F. per 1000 feet) no matter what the initial temperature is, nor at what altitude the process takes place.

The Lapse Rates

Comparison of this fixed adiabatic lapse rate of the vertical currents with the lapse rates present in the atmosphere, as measured by radiosonde ascents, forms a criterion of the conditions for soaring. Fig. 1 shows various possible lapse rates. The dotted lines show the adiabatic lapse rates.

From the ground up, there is indicated first a ground inversion marked A, starting with a surface temperature of 20° C. Suppose an upcurrent got started somehow, perhaps by the air being forced over a ridge. The upcurrent must vary its temperature according to the dotted line starting from 20°. Immediately the temperature of the upcurrent becomes considerably lower than the ambient temperature. At an elevation of 200 meters, the temperature is already about 5° C. That means the air that was forced up is considerably heavier than the surrounding air. It has a tendency to fall back to the surface, or rather in reality it would never get that high as it would rather flow around the ridge than over it. Ground inversions are encountered most frequently on calm clear nights. There can be no soaring in the altitude range covered by the inversion. All vertical air movements are choked.

Condition B in Fig. 1 indicates an extended stable lapse rate. If an upcurrent would get started at the highest temperature, it would follow the second dotted line. It is easy to see that again a negative temperature difference results. All upcurrents which might get started in the range of altitude from 200 meters to 800 meters on the graph would soon assume a lower temperature than the surroundings. All downcurrents would become warmer than the surroundings. While the choking is not so severe as in the inversion, it is sufficient to suppress or greatly diminish vertical movements. Stable lapse rates are common in "bad weather"; that is, in steady rain or when layers of stratus clouds are present. Soaring is very limited.

The isothermal layer C acts much like an inversion. Upcurrents that reach into it are quickly suppressed. Perhaps the best known isothermal region of the atmosphere is the stratosphere. Vertical exchange of air and moisture cannot penetrate deeply into it. Hence the lack of bumpiness and clouds in the stratosphere.

Condition D on Fig. 1 indicates a superadiabatic lapse rate, a theoretically ideal soaring condition. If the slightest vertical motion got under way anywhere in this region, the result would be an immediate increase in temperature difference, which is now positive. The higher the upcurrent goes, the lighter it becomes with regard to the surroundings. Its acceleration rapidly increases as it rises. Unfortunately the superadiabatic lapse rate is an unstable condition which cannot extend over a considerable range of height nor last very long. It is found near the ground, when intense heating of the ground takes place. At greater heights it is a rather rare phenomenon.

The lapse rate marked E in Fig. 1 is adiabatic. If a quantity of air in this layer somehow gets a push upward, it continues upward until the original impetus is used up by friction, because its temperature is the same as the outside temperature at all levels. The upcurrent is in equilibrium with the surroundings at all heights and no thermal forces tend to restrict the vertical motion at all. A "thermal" (a quantity of air which somehow got a little warmer than the surrounding air) stays warmer at all heights. The upcurrent is continuously accelerated upward until the excess temperature is dispersed by lateral mixing or until the adiabatic layer is traversed. Adiabatic lapse rates occur frequently in the atmosphere, near the ground as well as at greater heights. They are the rule on clear and windy days.

Fig. 1 contains an inversion F on top of the adiabatic lapse rate. If an upcurrent has formed underneath and has traveled through the adiabatic layer, it will push into the inversion on account of its inertia. As it proceeds, however, an increasing temperature difference between upcurrent and surroundings is formed. In other words, a downward force is now acting on the updraft, which makes it spread out horizontally and chokes it. Inversions limit the extent of altitude soaring. As a rule it is not possible for upcurrents to penetrate a well-defined inversion, and consequently one cannot soar through inversions. There are cases, however, where upcurrents are so warm and strong that they rupture a small and even moderate inversion and emerge with a temperature that is still in excess of that of the layer of air above the inversion, as is often the case with thunderstorm currents.

The Diurnal Variation of Soaring Conditions Near the Ground

The preceding paragraph shows the dependence of vertical air currents on the temperature lapse rates of the atmosphere, and it has been pointed out that the temperatures, especially those on the ground, are the result of radiation. During a twenty-four hour period, we go through one cycle of radiation, from maximum sunshine around noon to no sun at night to maximum sunshine around noon of the following day. Consequently the temperature variation on the ground goes through a twenty-four hour period with maximum temperatures sometime after noon, minimum temperatures after midnight to maximum temperatures again shortly after noon of the following day. The temperature variation on the ground causes a twenty-four hour variation of lapse rates in the lower layer of the atmosphere. In turn, chances for the formation of vertical currents vary on a twenty-four hour basis.

Fig. 2 and 3 give an indication of what occurs during a one-day period in the lowest 1000 to 3000 feet. It must be realized, however, that there are many other weather factors besides radiation which may superimpose on this picture and alter it considerably. The considerations apply under the assumption that the same type of weather is preserved for twenty-four hours. Two cases are considered: a clear calm day and a clear windy day.

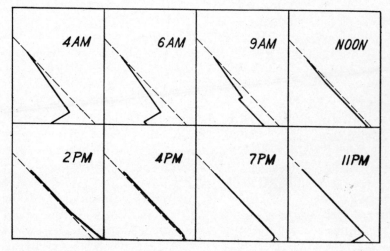

FIG. 2. THE DIURNAL VARIATION OF THE LAPSE RATE IN THE LAYER NEAR THE GROUND ON A CLEAR CALM DAY

At night there is a ground inversion; after sunrise the ground inversion begins to dissolve; in midday an adiabatic and, nearest the ground, a superadiabatic lapse rate forms; during the afternoon the air near the ground cools, aloft an adiabatic lapse rate remains; in the evening a new ground inversion develops.

The aerological radiosonde ascensions are carried out at 4:00 A.M. In the great majority of cases they reveal that at that time of the morning a ground inversion exists, as depicted in the first sketch of Fig. 2. A few hours later the sun rises and begins to warm the ground. The thin film of air directly over the ground receives heat from the ground and tiny eddies and whirls begin to form. Thus air particles that were in contact with the warm earth are carried upward and mixed with the cold air there. New heated elements follow, and by and by a layer is formed which has an adiabatic lapse rate and through which more and more heated air is exchanged from near the ground to the upper part of the inversion.

But the free exchange of currents from the ground to the upper layers of the atmosphere remains handicapped until the last of the ground inversion is wiped out. During the June-July Soaring Contests at Elmira, New York, it usually is 9:00 A.M. to 10:00 A.M. or even later before this is the case. Only from that time on do the thermals and ridge currents shoot up from the valley to great heights.

Then the energy of insolation serves to heat up the whole "turbulence zone." The lapse rate remains adiabatic and may even become superadiabatic and the mean temperature of the entire lower region of the atmosphere increases, as shown in the sketch for 2:00 P.M.

The maximum temperature of the day usually occurs at around 2 P.M. From then on the earth's surface begins to cool off as the sun declines. By about 5:00 P.M. the effect is quite noticeable in the atmosphere. The ground becomes cooler and so does the film of air that is in contact with it. That means that this air now becomes relatively heavy. It clings to the ground and resists being carried up by the turbulence and mixed with the higher layers. The cooler it gets, the more tenaciously it adheres to the ground. A new ground inversion then forms. At the same time, thermal conditions above may remain quite good. It is frequently observed that pilots continue to soar at heights of a few thousand feet after sundown, while it is impossible for others to get up to them from the ground.

During the night the ground inversion intensifies under the influence of the earth's radiation. And during the following day the cycle repeats itself unless a change of weather occurs. Fig. 4 shows actual air movement over an airport. A number of floating balloons were released from an airplane and their paths triangulated from the ground. All the balloons which were followed in the early morning hours went almost parallel with the ground. In contrast, the balloon of 11:30 A.M. shot up in a thermal of 500 to 600 feet per minute.

The diurnal variation of soaring conditions is different when a strong wind prevails. Fig. 3 illustrates what happens on such a day. At noon and shortly afterwards, the picture is similar to that of a calm day. There is an adiabatic layer from the ground up. When the ground begins to get colder, again a thin layer of cold air wants to form over it. But the strong wind with its turbulent structure picks up the cold air and carries it into the higher layers, all the time mixing it with the air which is already there. The result is that the turbulence preserves an adiabatic lapse rate and the cooling effect is distributed over the entire "turbulence zone." The mean temperature then drops. All this time energy has to be spent in lifting the heavy cold air off the ground. The energy is taken from the wind, which results in a decrease of wind velocity. Moreover, as the process goes on, the turbulence zone shrinks in height. Therefore, if an attempt is to be made to soar all night, a weather situation should be chosen in which the pressure gradient is large enough to guarantee that the wind will not die down during the night. Furthermore, a low ridge is preferred in order to be sure that it stays in the turbulence zone and does not get into the inversion on top of it. The diurnal temperature drop is less pronounced over water. Thus, chances of preserving an adiabatic lapse rate during the night are best for an on-shore wind.

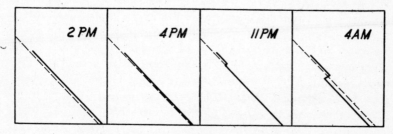

FIG. 3. THE VARIATION OF THE LAPSE RATE ON A CLEAR
WINDY DAY

In midday a high unstable layer exists; during the afternoon and evening, the mean temperature of the turbulence zone drops and the turbulence inversion becomes lower.

Thermals

It was shown that the temperature lapse rate governs the development of vertical currents once they get started. The initial upward movement is most frequently caused right at the surface of the earth, but at times also in greater heights. It may be caused mechanically or thermally; that is, we get slope winds or thermals. Frequently the two kinds form simultaneously or combine.

When the sun shines it heats the ground. Patches of good absorption and low heat capacity rise to high temperatures as, for instance, a desert or, on a smaller scale, any sandy spot. Other locations assume other temperatures according to their physical properties. If the ground is wet, a good portion of the energy received from the sun is spent on evaporation. It is well known that the diurnal temperature rise is delayed on mornings with dew. We know that woods stay cooler during the day, and ocean and lake regions offer coolness in spite of intense summer insolation.

Ground temperatures of 200° F. have been measured while the

air temperature, determined at 6 feet above ground, was less than 100°. This shows that the temperature gradient in the lowest 6 feet of the atmosphere can tremendously exceed the adiabatic lapse rate. This condition causes very great accelerations for any air particle moving up or down in this layer. The result is that tiny quantities of air shoot up and down at a great rate. This process can be seen with the mere eye as shimmering of the air. The very small particles of air mix readily with the air of the elevations into which they penetrate, causing a certain uniformity of temperature in the horizontal direction which makes it possible for this thermodynamically unstable condition to exist periods of 5 or 10 minutes or more.

On the other hand, a number of the tiniest turbulence elements in the 6-foot layer flow together, forming somewhat larger turbulence elements. The larger ones flow together and so on. Finally, like a trunk growing out of widespread fine roots, a mass of air which is warmer than the ambient air emerges from the atmospheric layer next to the ground. A thermal is born. It moves upward like a balloon, driven by its thermal acceleration and rising faster and faster and expanding more and more until it dies out at an altitude where the atmosphere is stable. As the upcurrent moves, new air flows in at the ground from the sides. This new air gradually becomes heated, tiny upcurrents flow together until after a while a new thermal emerges from the same spot. This may take 5 minutes and in other cases an hour or more.

Outside help frequently is required to make the thermal "break loose" and start upward. A gentle wind, penetrating into the layer next to the ground, will help to collect the scattered tiny upcurrents into one sizable one. This is particularly so when the process takes place on a slope, over which the wind has to climb, thus starting the updraft in the right direction. A nearby cold spot with air that has a tendency to flow under the warm air will release upcurrents. Soaring pilots who have flown over the Texas plains have always observed reliable upcurrents over the sandy beaches of the rivers, where undoubtedly the air over the relatively cold water assisted in causing thermals as much as the actual heating over the sand and mudflats. There is evidence that a glider pilot himself can help to release a thermal by maneuvering his ship over a place that is likely to produce an upcurrent. By stirring the air at a low altitude, a thermal, which is in formation, can be made to rise prematurely at the moment when it is needed to avoid an involuntary landing.

One major factor that spoils the formation of thermals is a high wind. It disrupts the process of collecting a sufficient number of little heated particles in the layer next to the ground into a sizable current. Even if a thermal upcurrent should emerge from this layer, it soon would be disrupted again by the turbulence of the high wind. Experience has shown that we have to rely upon other kinds of upcurrents when high wind velocities exist.

No hard and fast rules can be given as to where thermals are forming. Too much depends on the physics of the ground in relation to the surroundings, on the position of the sun, the wind direction and velocity. Many pilots depend on plowed fields, others favor wheat fields and beaches and a German pilot has made successful soaring flights with the help of a map of the ground

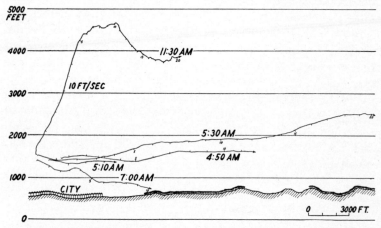

FIG. 4. TRAJECTORIES OF THE AIR OVER FLAT COUNTRY

Early in the morning when the atmosphere is stable the air flows almost parallel to the ground. In midday thermals and turbulence cause irregular currents.

The traces are the paths of floating balloons released between 5:00 and 7:00 A.M. and at 11:30 A. M.

water levels. Thermals, however, are formed by the combined action of various influences that repeat themselves. Once the search for thermals at a particular location has been successful, chances are that there will be an inexhaustible supply of upcurrents that can be utilized whenever the weather factors are essentially the same.

The size of thermals, too, varies with many factors. In order to utilize a thermal, it has to have a size that permits maneuvering a glider in it. Thermals are largest on calm days and when there is little chance for their release. On windy days, and under conditions that favor frequent release of updrafts, the currents are often so broken up that they can be recognized with the variometer but not utilized for soaring.

Where there are upcurrents there must be downcurrents. Luckily the general tendency is for upcurrents to spread out when they arrive at the higher stable layers. That distributes the downward motion over a larger space, resulting in gentle downcurrents over large areas. In contrast, most upcurrents have a comparatively high speed and are distributed over a small area. The glider pilot stays in these narrow fields by spiraling tightly.

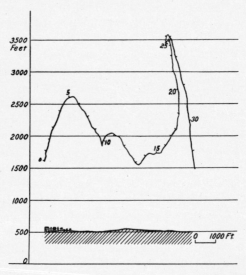

FIG. 5. MOTION OF AN AIR PARTICLE OVER FLAT COUNTRY ON A DAY WITH GOOD THERMALS

Note how the upcurrent is replaced by a downdraft in the same spot over the airport.

It is important to know that thermals seldom are chimneys of air going up constantly; rather, they are bubbles repeating themselves at intervals. Between two upcurrent bubbles there may be downcurrents at the same spot. Compare Fig. 5, which is the path of a floating balloon. It shows a thermal upcurrent changed into a downdraft within a period of a few minutes.

Thermals do not depend on high temperatures as such. What is necessary is that the ground has a higher temperature than the air. This is more frequently the case in spring and summer than in fall and winter. But there are very many occasions during the latter two seasons when thermals are plentiful. Clear days, on which the sun's radiation is most powerful, are often associated with cold waves. Cold polar air acquires a steep lapse rate before it reaches our latitudes. The ground is still warmer than the air. Both these factors favor the formation of thermals.

Evening Thermals

Similarly the occurrence of thermals is not restricted to daytime. During the day heat is being accumulated by the ground. Locations of high heat capacity, such as water, forests, swamps, and also cities store up great quantities of heat, even though this may not express itself in a great rise of temperature during the day. After sundown heat is sent out to space. As was shown above, the amount of radiation is proportional to the fourth power of temperature. Therefore, places that get very hot during the day cool very rapidly after sundown. Forests and similar places radiate more slowly and out of a vast storage of heat. As a result they now become the places over which thermals form. They are particularly active if they are elevated, for the nightly cooling effect on the air makes the lowest atmospheric layers heavy and sluggish. If this cold air can accumulate in valleys, thus allowing upper air with a lapse rate that is still adiabatic to flow over the heat reservoirs, large quiet upcurrent zones are created which last long into the night. Towns and cities should always be a source of good thermal upcurrents because their structure offers comparatively large surfaces to the sun, which results in the accumulation of much heat. Experience has shown, however, that the daytime upcurrents of cities and towns are often so broken up that they are useless to soaring. It is only in the evening that the turbulence diminishes and allows a large upcurrent field to form over the city.

Perhaps the most outstanding example of evening thermals is the upcurrent field that forms with a north wind over the city of Elmira and the wooded slopes of South Mountain near Elmira. It is here that thermals were first discovered by the famous pilot, Wolf Hirth.

Slope Currents

When a wind is referred to as having a certain velocity, the assumption is that what is meant is the mean velocity of the horizontal component of the wind over a certain period of time. For the wind does not flow in a steady stream parallel to the earth's surface; in addition to the horizontal flow there is a multitude of turbulent motions in the air. A gust usually is caused by an eddy component adding itself to the wind velocity; a lull is composed of the horizontal wind with the eddy motion going the other way. The wind varies all the time both in direction and velocity.

If the wind finds an obstacle in its way, like a mountain, it flows around and over it. We cannot draw an accurate picture of this flow, because it is just as little stationary as the wind that arrives at the obstacle. To depict the outstanding characteristics of the flow, we draw a picture as it would be, were the wind a non-turbulent medium. The glider pilot should always keep in mind that such presentations are idealized and only partly true. The flow over and around an obstacle changes abruptly, creating different currents from the ones shown in the picture. Fig. 6 gives an idea

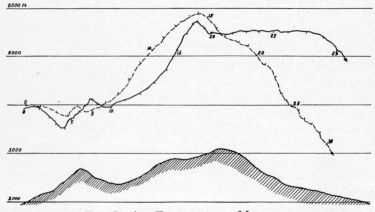

FIG. 6. AIR FLOW OVER A MOUNTAIN

The paths of two floating balloons, released simultaneously at the same spot, do not coincide. In lee one balloon indicates that a downcurrent exists. Five minutes later the other balloon has to float around a newly formed eddy.

of this. The graph shows the movements of two floating balloons, which were released simultaneously from an airplane and observed independently by two theodolite crews. Already during the first 5 minutes they had begun to follow different trajectories. One balloon reached the highest point after 14 minutes, the other one after 18. On the lee side of the mountain, one balloon indicated a smooth and fast downcurrent. The other one obviously traveled around an eddy that had formed in lee of the mountain.

Lifting air over an obstacle requires energy which can come only out of the wind energy. It can be shown, however, that there is not a sufficient amount of it available. That is, the air tends to go around the obstacle rather than over it and the wind velocity in front of the obstacle is reduced, especially in the lower layers. In the case of an extended mountainous area, this may cause very low wind velocities in the valleys. Only if a ridge is very wide compared to its height can we count on a flow of most of the air over the ridge. That is why comparatively low but extended slopes, like dunes, have proven to be more favorable for soaring than individual, though much higher, mountains. If the ridges lie in the form of a funnel, air is squeezed into a small space, making the wind velocity rise and thereby increasing the upward component of the wind. Many of our better soaring sites are so located. A long ridge rising out of flat country or water causes the most uniform and vigorous ridge upcurrents.

The smoother the change from flat country to the ridge, the smoother is the air flow. All steep grades and edges cause turbulence and eddies. If a ridge rises from flat country at an angle of steeper than 30°, it is likely that a windward eddy forms, inverting the wind direction at the slope. The least disturbance that must be expected is a shift of wind direction between valley and summit, caused by the retarding action of the ridge on the air streaming towards it.

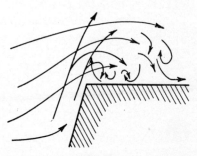

FIG. 7.   AIR CURRENTS ON THE WINDWARD SIDE OF A STEEP RIDGE

Almost horizontal flow may change abruptly into almost vertical flow. Strong turbulence exists also behind the edge.

The highest point reached by the air flowing over a ridge usually is found not over the summit but farther downwind. This is caused by the inertia of the air and in many cases by lee eddies, which, so to speak, extend the ridge farther back.

At very steep ridges, quarries, and the like a very turbulent flow forms. For a time the wind may go almost straight up, at other moments it flows almost horizontally, as shown in Fig. 7. This same flow may be encountered also over the edge of wooded areas.

A ridge may have a gentle slope, but suddenly flatten out into a plateau. Almost inevitably a turbulent zone of slow wind motion of a thickness of perhaps 200 feet results, above which the flow continues unabated (see Fig. 8).

Still more attention has to be paid to the lee side of the ridge. Lee eddies form there, wander off with the wind, and new ones form. Especially at steep hills, a small but very intense upcurrent field is created by the lee eddy, as shown in Fig. 9. It is very limited

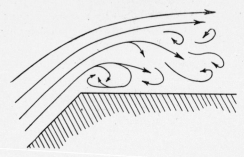

FIG. 8. THE TURBULENT ZONE OVER A PLATEAU

If a steep slope ends in a flat ridge top, the air continues to rise. A shallow turbulent zone exists over the plateau. The abrupt change of wind velocity with height makes landings dangerous.

in size and varies so abruptly that it may act on one wing of the glider, while the other wing is still in the less disturbed air.

Slope currents are modified by insolation. It has already been pointed out that thermals are easily released by the upcurrents of a slope. Thermals should be expected to form at the foot

FIG. 9. EDDY MOTION IN THE REAR OF THE RIDGE

An intense but narrow and variable upcurrent field is created by the eddy.

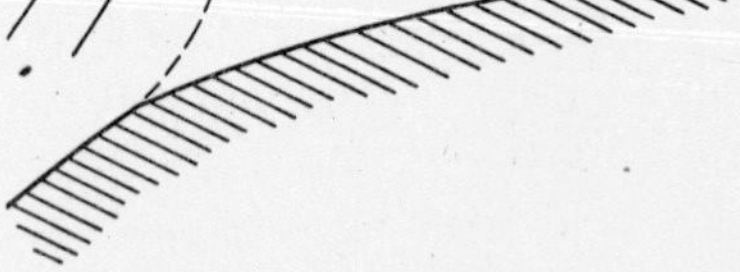

of the ridge. They go up at an angle, which is given by their rate of rise and the velocity of wind with which they float. This angle is usually much steeper than the slope of the

FIG. 10. COMBINED SLOPE CURRENT AND THERMAL

When the wind velocity is low and the sun shines on the lee side of a ridge, air may move up the ridge from all sides.

ridge, so that one has to fly out from the ridge toward the wind in order to find thermals.

If the sun beats on the slope, much heat is received by the ground which lies more or less vertical to the sun's rays. In such cases the ridge upcurrent is intensified and the highest point reached by the slope current is not as usual behind the ridge, but moves to windward over the slope. This was the case when the air current measurements of Fig. 6 were made.

Insolation may be most intense in back of the ridge. Under slow winds this results in a combined slope current and thermal. The air moves up the ridge on both sides, forming upcurrents well to the rear of the summit. Fig. 10 shows a schematic picture of this flow. Fig. 11 is an actual measurement.

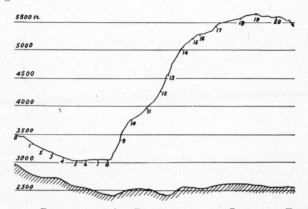

FIG. 11. PATH OF AN AIR PARTICLE IN THE LEE OF A RIDGE

A thermal has been released in lee of the ridge whose upward component exceeds the downdraft behind the ridge.

Humidity and Condensation

In the atmosphere all gases of which the atmosphere is composed, with the exception of water vapor, are found only in their gaseous state. But it is known that they can be forced into their liquid state if the temperature is lowered enough and if enough pressure is exerted.

Water vapor is exactly like the other gases, except that its critical temperature and pressure are well within the limits of the atmosphere. As long as it is a gas, it acts just like the other gases of the air. It is invisible and otherwise unnoticeable to our senses. Its presence is indicated only by special instruments, the hygrometers. It must be realized that clouds and fog do not consist of water vapor. They are formed of small drops of liquid water or small ice crystals.

As long as the water vapor remains a gas, it does not affect the thermodynamic processes in the air that were outlined above. But there are certain conditions under which part of the water vapor changes to water or ice. We notice this in the appearance of dew or frost, fog and clouds, and precipitation.

To understand the evaporation and condensation processes, we assume first that the atmosphere is entirely dry, that is, that it holds no water vapor whatsoever. The oceans and lakes contain liquid water; so do many places on land, particularly forests. This water wants to escape in gaseous form. The pressure with which the water wants to emerge as a gas from its reservoir of liquid is small. It is called the saturation water vapor pressure and depends on the temperature. If the water is warm, its vapor pressure is high. If the water temperature is lower, the vapor pressure is lower, but even ice has a certain vapor pressure with which it wants to escape as a gas. This is impressively demonstrated by the gradual disappearance of snow and ice from the ground, though the temperature may stay below the freezing point. Fig. 12 shows how the saturation vapor pressure varies with temperature.

From the oceans, and so on, water vapor now escapes as a gas into the air which is assumed to have the same temperature as the water. The water vapor mixes with the other components and is carried into higher layers by turbulent exchange. The air begins to contain measurable quantities of water vapor, as shown by a hygrometer reading.

As the evaporation from the water surface or from forests or the like continues, the air increases its vapor content until the partial gas pressure of water vapor equals that at the water's surface. At that point emanation of water vapor from the surface naturally must stop. The air is saturated. Its humidity is 100 per cent. We say the "relative humidity" is 100 per cent.

As Fig. 12 shows, the saturation pressure varies with temperature.

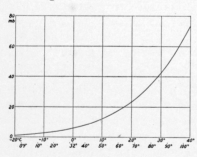

FIG. 12. SATURATION WATER VAPOR PRESSURE AS A FUNCTION OF TEMPERATURE

We now imagine the saturated air to move over dry land; the humidity remains unchanged so long as the temperature remains the same. However, if heating takes place, then saturation or 100 per cent relative humidity would correspond to a higher vapor pressure than is actually there. So, we now have only a certain percentage of the full possible quota of water vapor. The relative humidity has become less than 100 per cent.

On the other hand we may have cooling instead of heating. That means our air would hold more water vapor than its full possible quota. We get more than 100 per cent relative humidity or super-saturation. That is an unstable condition which cannot last, if the excess vapor gets a chance to change back to liquid water. It will do this by falling out on whatever is available. Usually, enough small particles of hygroscopic dust and salt are contained in the air to serve as condensation nuclei. Around them the excess water collects in the form of tiny drops; that is, we get fog or clouds.

The humidity of the air up to great heights is also measured daily by aerological ascents. It varies greatly from day to day and in different layers of the atmosphere. Air masses that travel over maritime regions pick up plenty of moisture, particularly when they are warm. Typically moist is the air that reaches North America after sweeping over the Gulf of Mexico. On the other hand, continental air masses are generally dry, particularly when they come from polar regions where there is less evaporation from the ground on account of the low temperatures.

The humidity of the air can be expressed by various units of humidity. Most commonly it is referred to as "relative humidity"; that is, the ratio between the actual water vapor content to the largest amount possible at the given temperature. Meteorologists use also the terms "vapor pressure" (in millibars or in mm. or inches of mercury), "specific humidity" (in grams of water vapor per kilogram of air), "absolute humidity" (in grams of water vapor per cubic meter of air), and "wet bulb temperature." For aviation purposes, the humidity is often expressed by the "dew point temperature." The dew point is that temperature to which the air would have to be cooled in order to be saturated. In other words, if the air would be cooled just beyond the dew point, fog or clouds would form.

The Heat of Condensation and Condensation Adiabatic Lapse Rates

A certain amount of heat is needed in order to change liquid water into water vapor. To evaporate 1 gram of water of a temperature t requires an amount of heat of $597.83 - 0.647\,t$. For example, when boiling water is evaporated, 533 calories are needed for each cc. of water. That is about six times as much heat as it required to heat the same cc. of water from room temperature to the boiling point! The large heat requirements of evaporation are noticed in everyday life. When water evaporates from our skin, we feel a chill, because the heat that is used for the evaporation is taken out of the skin.

When water vapor changes back to liquid water, the same amount of heat is liberated again. Assume that a quantity of air is cooled below its dew point; condensation begins to take place and the corresponding heat is supplied to the air. As a result, the cooling process becomes retarded. However, the air temperature will not actually rise because in this case the droplets would evaporate again immediately.

The amount of water vapor contained in the air when saturation exists depends on the temperature of the air, as shown in Fig. 12. Therefore, if condensation takes place at high temperatures, more water condenses than at low temperatures. The amount of heat of condensation liberated must therefore be higher at higher temperatures or, in other words, the retarding effect on a certain cooling rate of the air becomes larger at high temperatures.

The temperature in upcurrents drops according to the adiabatic lapse rate; that is, 1° C. for every 100 meters of ascent. During this process the temperature may fall below the dew point. At that moment condensation sets in and the rate at which the air cools is retarded; more so at higher temperatures. The adiabatic lapse rate changes into another, smaller one. This new lapse rate is called the condensation adiabatic lapse rate (also called moist adiabatic or pseudo-adiabatic lapse rate). Near the ground the condensation adiabatic lapse rate is:

30	20	10	0	−10	−20	−30° C.
86	68	50	32	14	−4	−22° F.
0.37	0.44	0.54	0.62	0.75	0.86	0.91° C. per 100 meters.

It varies somewhat with altitude, but the processes involved are too complex to be explained here. Meteorologists use "adiabatic charts" which show in graphical form not only the adiabatic lapse rate, but also the condensation adiabatic lapse rates for all temperatures and pressures.

Cumulus Clouds

Cumulus clouds are the billowy, often mountainous types of good weather clouds that form on days on which there is enough moisture in the air to lead to condensation when thermal or slope currents ascend. At first the upcurrent follows the dry adiabatic rate until condensation begins. Neglecting the expansion of the water vapor as it is carried upward, we can say that the first cloud droplets form when the dew point, as measured on the ground, is reached by the cooling process in the upcurrent. For all practical purposes, we compute the altitude of the cloud base as the difference between temperature and dew point temperature in Centigrade degrees multiplied by 100. For example, if the temperature is 25° C., the dew point 10° C., then the cloud base is found at $(25 - 10) \times 100$ = 1500 meters or about 1650 feet. Taking into account the fall in dew point owing to expansion of rising air, the cloud base is roughly at as many thousand meters as one eighth the difference between air temperature and dew point in C. degrees, or at as many thousand feet as one fourth the difference in F. degrees.

Formation of cumulus clouds has two distinct advantages. First, the upcurrents are now crowned by clouds; that is, they are almost visible and can be found easily. Secondly, the original upcurrent is greatly intensified by the heat of condensation. The above table shows that the condensation adiabatic lapse rate is less than the dry adiabatic. That implies that cloud upcurrents can easily pene-

Photo by Prof. Alexander McAdie, Blue Hill Observatory, Harvard University

FIG. 13. CUMULUS CLOUDS

trate into and even continue to receive additional lift from stable layers in the atmosphere. Meteorologists talk about "conditional instability," a condition where the actual measured lapse rate of the atmosphere is steeper than the condensation adiabatic rate. Such a condition may exist over a large vertical extent. If a thermal or a slope current ascends into such a layer, it puts all the available energy to work and tremendous cumulus clouds with very great vertical wind velocities form. They are called cumulonimbus. Up-currents of over 50 feet per second have been found in such clouds. Frequently electric disturbances are connected with such overgrown cumuli; we then have local thunderstorms. In 1939 the American altitude record was more than doubled by a flight into such a thunderstorm.

The meteorologist can compute the size of upcurrents in cumulus clouds from the temperature and humidity distribution of the atmosphere, and measurements by glider pilots have verified such computations. With some experience the pilot himself can readily form an opinion on the intensity of the vertical currents in a cumulus cloud. The bulging edges of the cumuli give an impressive picture of the mighty forces at work. But the air movement at the edges is greatly reduced by the friction between the ascending mass of air in the cloud and the free atmosphere. Inside, the vertical speeds are even larger, though it is reported that the motion is more uniform compared to the turbulent boundary.

F. Ellerman, Mt. Wilson Observatory

FIG. 14. CUMULO-NIMBUS ("THUNDERHEAD")

Some ten years ago much research by Peter Riedel and the author, then with the German Research Institute for Soaring, was spent on finding out if there is any regularity in the upcurrent field of a cumulus cloud. For this purpose hundreds of systematic flights were carried out. A small airplane with recording meteorological instruments attached under its wings was taken under a cumulus, then the engine was stopped entirely and the ship glided down, circling under the cloud. The barograph recordings of the plane allowed exact determination of the vertical currents encountered, as Fig. 15 shows. Ground crews measured the motion of the cloud and the position of the plane in regard to the cloud. It could not be established that any particular part of the cumulus cloud would regularly furnish better lift than other parts. Still, a number of soaring pilots maintain that better lifts are obtained on the windward side of cumuli and on the side exposed to the sun.

More important to practical soaring are the experimental results concerning the variation of upcurrent intensity with time. Like a thermal, a cumulus cloud is not stationary. It forms, builds up, decreases and disappears. The life cycle of a cumulus cloud varies from a few minutes to several hours. It can be determined easily in each case by observation of the clouds. When a cumulus is created, as described above, very small droplets form first. They are suspended in the air, having only a very low rate of fall. But all the time small drops grow and coalesce, forming bigger ones. These fall faster. If their rate of fall exceeds the upcurrent, they might even come to the ground in the form of a shower. Though this is not usually the case with ordinary cumuli, comparatively large amounts of water collect in large drops in the lower part of the cloud.

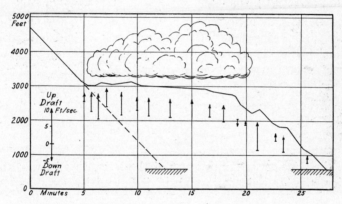

FIG. 15. UPCURRENTS UNDER A CUMULUS CLOUD

The normal sinking speed of the airplane is shown by the steep line from left to center bottom. The barograph trace shows the actual loss of altitude under the cumulus. The arrows are the upcurrents as computed from the difference of actual and normal sinking speed of the plane.

The original thermal bubble shoots up through its adiabatic state, then through its condensation adiabatic state; it finally reaches a region of the atmosphere, perhaps an inversion, where the upcurrent particles become heavier than the surroundings. On account of inertia, the advance part of the upcurrent pushes deeply into the inversion. After the energy of movement is spent, the particles tend to sink again. But they meet the rest of the upcurrent which still tends to go up. So the currents spread out sideways. If this process is pronounced, the cloud takes on the shape of a huge anvil.

After all of the bubble has bumped into the inversion, the entire mass of air swings back to earth. It is now distributed over a larger space so that the downcurrent is slow. Nevertheless, the droplets in the upper part of the cloud evaporate at a fair rate as they are carried into lower warmer regions. It takes some time for the downcurrent to proceed to the lower part of the cloud. In this region, as shown above, there is an accumulation of large drops, which it takes some time to evaporate. This shows that the cloud remains in existence for some time while downcurrents are active.

Cloud Streets and Waves

The type of cumulus clouds best liked for soaring is the one just described. Its formation is caused by thermals and occasionally by slope currents. It occurs on calm days and when moderate winds prevail. On stormy days the cumulus takes on another shape.

High winds are very turbulent because all the obstacles on the ground over which the wind passes cause innumerable eddies and irregular currents to form, which float along with the wind, only slowly diminishing under the influence of friction and possible thermal forces. The continuous action of all the up- and down-currents causes a general adiabatic lapse rate to be established in the turbulence zone. Compare Fig. 3. The mean temperature of the layer over which the turbulence spreads remains the same. If there was originally a stable lapse rate or an inversion, we get now a temperature rearrangement so that the temperature rises at the ground and decreases at the upper end of the turbulence zone with the same mean temperature of the layer. In that way an inversion, the "turbulence inversion," is formed between the turbulence zone and the upper atmosphere. If heating takes place at the ground, the temperature of the entire turbulence zone with its adiabatic lapse rate goes up. Therefore the turbulence inversion becomes smaller and may even disappear.

If the moisture content in the turbulence zone is high enough, condensation takes place and cumulus clouds form. In spite of their heat of condensation, however, they cannot shoot up freely because of the turbulence inversion. In contrast to the "heat cumuli," the "turbulence cumuli" are flat; the more so, the more pronounced is the turbulence inversion. In contrast to the "heat cumuli," the "turbulence cumuli" have a pronounced upcurrent region to the windward and downcurrents, downwind, where they dissolve.

Turbulence cumuli are no good for altitude soaring. But it happens frequently that a certain regularity in the turbulence causes the turbulence cumuli to arrange themselves in a quasi-regular pattern. That greatly facilitates distance soaring along chains of such clouds.

Not infrequently turbulence develops into a regular rolling motion, particularly in the lee of long-stretched mountain ranges, from which large lee eddies float off. Then we get long-stretched cloud banks of stratocumulus arranged all over the sky in long bands and ribbons. They may be arranged perpendicular to the wind direction, but are also known to form parallel with the wind. Upcurrents are found under the clouds, downcurrents in the open spaces. This is a favorable condition for long-distance soaring.

Turbulence cumuli are not bound to a turbulence zone near the ground. In fact they may form on top of a ground inversion, if a strong wind blows over the layer of air next to the surface. If the wind blows over water or sand, waves are formed. Similarly, air waves form in the ground inversion layer when the upper air flows over it. These waves are much larger in size than the water and sand waves and apt to topple over. Thus turbulence starts and penetrates both downward into the inversion and upward into the layer of high wind. If there is sufficient moisture, turbulence cumuli come into existence.

Fig. 16. Altocumuli

The same process of wave formation is what causes the mackerel sky; that is, high clouds of the cumulus type (see Fig. 16). Altocumuli are most common at altitudes of from 10,000 to 15,000 feet. They form from air waves caused by wind shifts at inversions at these elevations. Since such clouds are not subject to diurnal variations, they might become an important source of upcurrents for duration flights. German attempts to soar under altocumulus clouds after airplane tow were promising.

Polar Front and Air Masses

On previous pages occasional reference was made to "air masses." The "air mass analysis" for weather forecasting is now widely employed in this country and familiarity with its concepts is most useful to the glider pilot. However, the subject is too broad to be treated fully here. Only a general outline can be given with some emphasis on the cold front which is particularly important for soaring.*

If the same train of thought that led to the explanations of thermals is applied to the atmosphere as a whole, we would conclude that permanent upcurrents exist over the equatorial regions, where the heating by the sun is most intense. Then downcurrents should be the rule over the cold polar regions. A general circulation would result in such a manner that the northern hemisphere would have prevailing north winds near the ground and south winds aloft. This simple scheme, however, is spoiled for two reasons. First, because of the presence of continents and oceans. In summer the land is warm compared to the water. A circulation from water to land in the lower atmospheric layers and a flow from land to water at greater heights results. In winter this process works the other way around. The trade winds are the result of this action between land and water.

Secondly, there is the rotation of the earth. When air leaves the North Polar region, traveling south toward the equator, it has little east-west or west-east velocity and tends to continue straight south. The earth rotates from west to east and the velocity of the earth's surface increases as the distance from the axis increases; that is, the farther away we go from the pole. The result is that the earth, so to speak, slips away under the air towards the east. We notice this relative motion as an east wind.

Since the circumference of the earth increases as we go south from the North Pole the air from the small polar region distributes over a larger and larger area as it proceeds south, so that its southward component of movement gradually diminishes. At a latitude of about 65° nothing is left but an east wind blowing around the earth.

It can be shown similarly that the air which starts north from the equatorial regions is gradually bent over into a west wind. This current covers our latitudes, hence our prevailing westerly winds.

At a latitude of about 65° we now have a cold easterly current

---

* For more detailed information, the book on *Aeronautical Meteorology* by George F. Taylor is recommended.

on one side and a warm westerly current on the other side. The demarcation line is called the polar front.

What happens is depicted in Fig. 17. Waves form. On account of the small density difference between the polar and the equatorial air, the waves are of tremendous size, extending over hundreds of miles.

Fig. 17 shows how a wave, formed at the polar front, changes over a period of time. Warm air penetrates the cold region and in back cold air sweeps around into the originally warm region. But the relative movements of the warm air and cold air are more complicated than that. The air moves not only in the horizontal, but also in the vertical direction; the warmer and therefore lighter

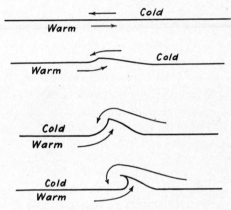

FIG. 17. WAVES IN THE POLAR FRONT

air slides up over colder air, which sweeps around, and pushes under the warm air.

Fig. 18 shows one phase of such a wave in greater detail. The lower part of the drawing corresponds to the presentation in the previous figure. The upper part is a vertical cross section through the line *AB*.

On the ground we find the warm air only in the triangular southern section, the "warm sector." The line where the warm air begins to slide from the surface up over the cold air is the warm front. The line which separates cold and warm air where cold air advances is called a cold front.

Along the warm front surface, the warm and relatively moist air moves slowly upward, too slowly to furnish upcurrents for soaring. As it comes under lower pressure, it cools. More cooling is caused by a certain amount of mixing between the cold and warm air along the warm front surface. Consequently, extended cloudiness is caused, beginning with cirrostratus at great heights down to stratus and fog. Long stretches of steady rain accompany the passage of the warm front surface. There is good warm weather in the warm sector, but the northwest current that brings the polar air around behind the cold front lets the temperature drop abruptly when it passes.

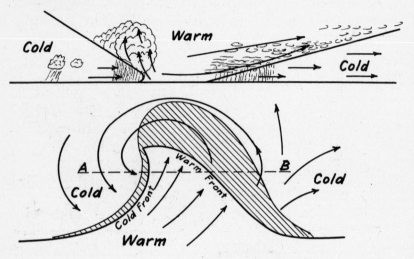

FIG. 18. DISTRIBUTION OF WIND, TEMPERATURE AND CLOUDINESS
IN A "LOW"

At the warm front warmer air slides up on top of colder air. At the cold front
polar air pushes under warm air.

The whole phenomenon, as presented in Fig. 18, is idealized, but can often enough be recognized clearly on the weather map. If isobars are drawn, it is found that we have the detailed structure of a "low." The wave moves away from the place of its origin and travels along in our prevailing westerly current. All the time its own development, the play between colder and warmer air, continues.

The Cold Front

A cold front can be hundreds, even thousands, of miles long. It stretches out in a sweeping line, traveling from west to east at a speed the order of magnitude of which is 25 to 40 miles per hour. The heavy cold air behind it drives the warmer air in front out of the way and upward, much as a wedge would that is driven under it. If the warm air is particularly warm, that is, light in places, and if it is quite unstable, less energy is required to remove it. In this case the cold air advances faster and the front bulges out. On the other hand, the front may get retarded. If there is a mountain range in the way, the cold air is held back until enough has accumulated to flow over the range. By this time much of the cold air has advanced around the mountains. The gap in the front may close again behind the obstacle before the cold air reaches as high as the mountain tops. Naturally the sudden lifting process of the front is thereby greatly reduced and broken up within the mountain region.

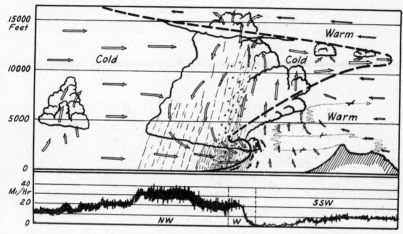

FIG. 19. THE PASSAGE OF A FRONTAL THUNDERSTORM
(COMPARE TEXT)

Fig. 19 shows the schematic picture of a front passage, based on actual measurements. The lower part of the drawing contains a reproduction of the trace of a wind-registering instrument. Reading from right to left, there was a 10 m.p.h. SSW wind, the air movement in the warm sector. Compare Fig. 18. Very shortly before the arrival of the front, the wind died down. The calm before the storm! Then, as the cold air broke in, the wind on the ground shifted over west to northwest and jumped up to a maximum of 41 m.p.h. Had there been a temperature registration, it would have shown a temperature drop of many degrees during this short period.

In the upper part of Fig. 19 the warm air is indicated toward the right, the cold air toward the left. The actual boundary line between the two is doubtful. It cannot easily be measured because nobody wants to fly into such regions for the sake of scientific measurements. And even then the measurements would be difficult to interpret because of the adiabatic and condensation adiabatic changes taking place when the vertical movements get under way. From experiments with models and from the measurements of air currents that were occasionally made by unlucky glider pilots who happened to fly into this region, we believe that the picture corresponds closely to the actual conditions. Where the "head" of the cold air rushes in, a tremendous eddy, often a regular roll, forms. That accounts for the gust which accompanies the passage of a front. In front of this roll and over it the warm air is thrown upward. Condensation takes place, a tremendous cumulonimbus builds up all along the line of the front. It destroys stable conditions and inversions, though the altitudes at which inversions used to be are often still indicated by the fanning out of the thundercloud at various heights.

The upcurrent field starts away out in the warm air. As the upward movement continues, heavy black clouds form at that place; that is, the front moves on. The clouds are the result of condensation. As shown before, the heat of condensation increases the upcurrents. The highest vertical velocities and the greatest turbulence are found in the forward part of the clouds. The upcurrents sustain the clouddrops. They also sustain the raindrops, which form by growth and coalescence from clouddrops, for even the largest raindrops fall only with a velocity of about 20 feet per second. At some altitude the temperature goes below freezing; ice crystals form. They collect cloud droplets around themselves, creating pellets composed of ice and water.

These may fall for a while. But if a current moves them up below the freezing point again, they coat with a layer of ice, and we get hail. All these raindrops, pellets, and hail are shoved back by the big eddy current. When they arrive in the region of the downward branch of the eddy, they fall through fast because the downcurrent increases their own rate of fall. The precipitation arrives on the ground shortly after the big gust has passed.

After the period of the precipitation, the front has passed. We are now in the cold air mass, which gradually increases in thickness. As it flows over the ground, which is still warm and wet, the lower layers are heated and supplied with moisture. Cumulus clouds form and soaring conditions become excellent, to the consolation of those pilots who have missed connecting with the upcurrent field in the warm air just ahead of the front.

There is only one rule to front soaring, but it is all-important: always stay in front of the big thundercloud and never allow it to catch up with you. The inside of a frontal thunderstorm is, to say the least, unpleasant.

The Moazagotl Condition

In recent years the attention of both glider pilots and meteorologists has been focused on a condition which permits soaring to very great heights, more than 20,000 feet, with comparative ease. It is now known that this condition can exist at various places all over the world. It was first discovered in the Sudeten Mountains in Germany. Many generations ago the inhabitants began to observe that occasionally a large, isolated cirrus cloud formed at great heights. This cloud proved to be the forerunner of bad weather and is used by the natives as a weather indicator. They named it "Moazagotl," which is Silesian dialect and may be freely translated into something like "foe's beard."

The weatherwise members of a glider school located in this region paid due attention to the Moazagotl cloud, and soon found that soaring conditions were greatly improved when it was in existence. As the experiences of many soaring flights were pieced together, the following picture evolved. With a wind velocity of about 40 m.p.h. the usual lee eddy behind a mountain range stretching out perpendicular to the wind is not formed. Instead, there is a continuous strong downcurrent. But 5 miles farther back, a strong upcurrent field exists. Behind the upcurrent field, downcurrents follow, then a new upcurrent field, 5 miles distant from the first, a third region of downcurrents and a third region of upcurrents, again about 5 miles farther back and all parallel with the mountain range. The fields of up- and downcurrents do not move with the wind, but are stationary. In the atmosphere near the ground, remarkable wind shifts occur. In some places the wind direction is entirely opposite to the prevailing wind. At great heights the huge cirrus cloud, consisting of ice crystals, caps the entire region.

Since the glider school is located under the third upcurrent region, flights were at first made there. Later it was found that even better conditions existed in the second field, and in September 1937 a flight into the first region and deeply into the Moazagotl cloud led to the then record altitude of 22,000 feet.

After an exhaustive study of the condition, the following explanation of the phenomenon has been offered. It is illustrated by Fig. 20.

If the weather situation causes a flow of air which is cold in the layers next to the ground and if a mountain range is in the path of this air, then the cold air will collect on the windward side of the range until it reaches high enough to flow through the mountain passes and finally over the entire ridge. On the lee side, however, the cold air flows off quickly into the center of the low. There will develop a difference in level of the cold air. It is high in front of the range, low behind it. The warmer air current aloft approaches with great velocity and, falling down the precipice of cold air, forms large standing waves which extend through the entire atmosphere up to the stratosphere. If the warm air is sufficiently unstable and moist, the amplitude of the waves increases with height and a Moazagotl cloud forms. The waves have a length of from 4 to 6 miles; the amplitude in the lower layers is only about 1500 feet. At times the waves may work their way down to the ground, but usually a number of large "rolls" of air form near the ground, filling out the space under the crests of the waves. The diameter

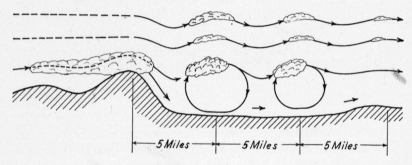

FIG. 20. THE AIR CURRENTS OF THE MOAZAGOTL CONDITION

Near the ground there are stationary rolls; aloft standing waves of amplitude that increase with height are capped by a cirrus cloud.

of these rolls is approximately the same as the height of the mountain range, and the upward branches have also a sufficient vertical velocity for soaring. The Moazagotl condition is more frequent during the colder seasons of the year.

Such conditions have not yet been used by American glider pilots, although they are known to exist here. The records of the observatory on Mt. Weather in Virginia contain observations of Moazagotl clouds behind the Blue Ridge Mountains, and the author has observed the same phenomenon from Mt. Washington Observatory in New Hampshire. It will require some patient experimenting to locate exactly the upcurrent fields and to pick the correct weather situation. But there is a decided opportunity for exceeding the American, if not the international, altitude record.

CHAPTER VII

INSTRUMENTS

By Charles H. Colvin

ALTHOUGH IT IS BEST to give primary instructions in a glider unequipped with any instruments, several are useful for soaring. For maximum performance of a modern sailplane at least six are necessary. These are in order of their importance: variometer, altimeter, airspeed indicator, turn and bank indicator, compass and clock. Some pilots may argue the relative importance of the turn and bank, the airspeed, and the altimeter, but all will agree that the most essential is the variometer. However, the first used in gliding is the airspeed indicator so it will be described first.

AIRSPEED INDICATOR

The airspeed indicator shows the rate at which the glider is moving through the air. It is a differential pressure gauge which is actuated by the pressure difference generated in a pitot-static or pitot-venturi tube.

Two tube lines connect the instrument to the pressure tube, which is mounted in a position where it receives an undisturbed flow of air.

The indication of the airspeed indicator depends upon the density and temperature, as well as upon the speed of the air. It is graduated in units of speed for "standard" atmospheric conditions; that is, barometric pressure of 29.92 in. of mercury (1013 millibars) and a temperature of 15° C. For other pressures and temperatures corrections must be applied.

The airspeed indicator is shown in Fig. 1, in which the inside of the diaphragm is connected to the pitot tube, and the case (outside of the diaphragm) is connected to the static or venturi tube. Increase of air speed causes increase in the pressure difference and expansion of the diaphragm. This lifts the wire bridge and the arm which rests upon it. The movement of the arm turns the rocking-shaft and its arm which presses against the sector arm. The latter turns the sector, which engages the pinion, turning it and the hand. The hairspring keeps all parts in contact with each other.

The face of the airspeed indicator is seen in Fig. 2. A typical pitot-static tube is illustrated in Fig. 3.

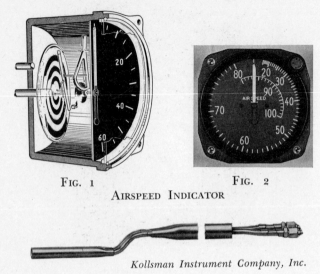

FIG. 1   FIG. 2

AIRSPEED INDICATOR

Kollsman Instrument Company, Inc.

FIG. 3. PITOT-STATIC TUBES FOR AIR SPEED

ALTIMETER

The altimeter shows the altitude of the glider in relation to sea level or to the earth. It is an absolute pressure gauge the dial of which is marked in units of altitude.

The altimeter operates from the difference in pressure inside and outside an airtight diaphragm. The pressure outside the diaphragm is that of the inside of the instrument's case, which is airtight and is connected to the static tube of a pitot-static tube. This connection is generally joined to the static connection of the airspeed indicator. The pressure on the diaphragm is therefore the same as that of the outside air at the static opening of the pitot-static tube.

Altimeter readings are correct only under "standard" conditions; that is, when the barometric pressure at sea level is 29.92 inches of mercury, the temperature at sea level is 15° C. (59° F.), the temperature gradient is 1.98° C. (3.56° F.) per 1000 feet, and the barometric scale of the altimeter is set to 29.92 inches. Under all other conditions, to obtain the altitude, corrections must be made for pressure by setting the altimeter barometric scale to the altimeter sea level pressure, and for temperature, by the use of tables or a computer.

Kollsman Instrument Company, Inc.

FIG. 4.   SENSITIVE ALTIMETER

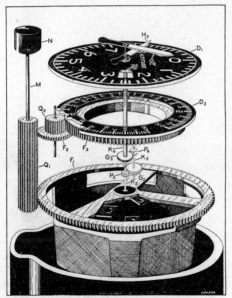

Kollsman Instrument Company, Inc.

FIG. 5.   SENSITIVE ALTIMETER

The operating and setting mechanisms of the Kollsman Sensitive Altimeter are shown in Fig. 4 and 5. The diaphragm D expands as the outside pressure is reduced, moving a link L_1 and arm A_1 and thus turning rocking-shaft R. The weight of the diaphragm is balanced by balance arm B which is supported by spring E and is connected to the rocking-shaft by link L_2 and arm A_2. Rocking-shaft R carries sector S, which drives pinion P_1 on shaft K_1, which also carries gear G_2, and hairspring C. Gear G_1 drives pinion P_2 on shaft K_2, which also carries pinion P_3 and the long hand H_1.

FIG. 6. KOLLSMAN
SENSITIVE ALTIMETER

Referring now to Fig. 5, pinion P_3 drives gear G_3 through G_2 and pinion P_4. Gear G_3 is on shaft K_4, which also carries the short hand H_2. Dial D_1 is fixed in the case, but dial D_2, together with the mechanism, is turned by turning knob N. This, through stem M and pinion Q_1, turns gears F_1, and F_2, Gear F_1 turns the mechanism directly and gear F_2 turns the dial D_2 through pinion Q_2 and gear F_3.

The face of the altimeter is seen in Fig. 6.

BALL BANK INDICATOR

The ball bank indicator is shown in Fig. 10B. It consists of a ball within a curved glass tube. The tube is filled with liquid except for an air bubble which is left in a standpipe at one end of the tube (out of sight). When a turn indicator is used the bank indicator is usually combined with it. The ball bank is helpful in keeping the sailplane level laterally in straightaway flight and essential in making turns of narrow diameter when the sailplane is steeply banked, especially in cloud flying.

VARIOMETER

The variometer is also known as a climb indicator or a vertical speed indicator. It shows the rate of change of altitude of the glider and is operated by the rate of change of atmospheric pressure.

The capillary leak type of variometer as made by Kollsman, Pioneer, and Askania, comprises a sensitive differential pressure gauge, an air chamber (usually heat insulated), and a leak tube.

The Kollsman instrument, as illustrated diagrammatically in Fig. 7, has the insulated chamber (not shown in the picture) within the instrument case, the mechanism being within the chamber. The inside of the diaphragm is connected directly to the outside air through a static tube (which may be the static tube of the airspeed indicator pitot-static tube), while the outside of the diaphragm is subject to the pressure of the air in the chamber, which is connected to the outside air through a leak tube.

As the glider rises, the pressure inside the diaphragm becomes less than that in the chamber outside the diaphragm and the diaphragm moves inward. Amplifying mechanism transmits the movement to the hand, causing it to move up.

The face of the instrument is seen in Fig. 8.

The Cobb-Slater variometer employs two tapered tubes, the "leaks" being variable in accordance with the position of a small indicating pellet in each tube. This instrument is shown diagram-

FIG. 7. VARIOMETER   FIG. 8. KOLLSMAN VERTICAL
                                SPEED INDICATOR

matically in Fig. 9A. The size of the tapered tubes is greatly exaggerated in the picture.

The top of the UP tube and the bottom of the DOWN tube are connected to the outside air, while the bottom of the UP tube and the top of the DOWN tube are connected to an air chamber. As the glider rises, the relatively greater pressure in the chamber causes air to flow out. As the pellet in the DOWN tube is at the bottom, sealing the tube, no air can flow through this tube. It therefore goes through the UP tube, lifting the pellet in this tube until the passageway around the pellet is sufficient to balance the pressure difference. The height the pellet is lifted is a measure of the rate of ascent.

Similarly, as the glider goes down the air flows from the outside to the chamber and as it cannot pass the pellet at the bottom of the UP tube it lifts the pellet in the DOWN tube until the leakage past the pellet is sufficient to balance the pressure.

The face of the Cobb-Slater variometer is seen in Fig. 9B.

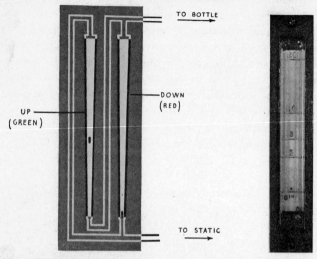

A. Diagrammatic Sketch B. Face

FIG. 9. COBB-SLATER VARIOMETER

TURN INDICATOR

The turn indicator is shown diagrammatically in Fig. 10A. A venturi tube through which air flows as the glider advances creates a vacuum which exhausts the air from the instrument case. The incoming air impinges upon the buckets of a gyro wheel, rotating it at a high speed. The gyro axis is normally horizontal and athwartship, in a frame which is supported in pivots on an axis which is horizontal and fore and aft. Turning about the vertical causes the gyro frame to move about the fore and aft axis against the force of a restraining spring, thus measuring the turn. The venturi

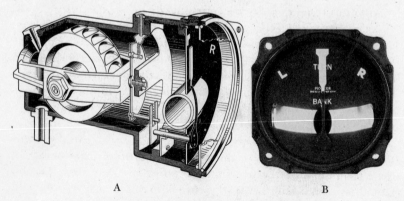

A

B

FIG. 10. TURN AND BANK INDICATOR

should, if possible, be so mounted that it may be retracted when not in use.

To overcome the objections of aerodynamic drag of the large size venturi necessary to drive a glider turn indicator and the possibility of ice formations making the instrument inoperative while flying, an electric type has been developed by Siemens in Germany. In this instrument the electric motor is incorporated as the gyro. It is driven by a 12-volt dry cell battery.

A ball bank indicator is usually combined with the turn indicator. The face of the combined instrument appears in Fig. 10B.

CLINOMETER

A fore and aft clinometer (sometimes erroneously called a "pitch indicator") comprises a triangular-shaped glass tube half full of liquid, and is graduated to show fore and aft angles. Being affected by acceleration as well as by angles, it is accurate as a clinometer only when the glider is flying at a constant speed.

COMPASS

The compass consists of a pair of magnets universally supported on a pivot within a bowl of liquid. The magnets are usually carried in or on a float to reduce the weight on the pivot. The float carries a graduated card, or rose, which turns in respect to, and is read against, a lubber's line. Compensation is provided for removing the effects of the local magnetism of the glider.

Kollsman Instrument Co.

FIG. 11. COMPASS

A typical compass is seen in Fig. 11.

CLOCK

The clock is a useful member of the instrument family requiring no special description. A standard aircraft clock incorporates a sweep second hand, and numbers only the hours of 12, 3, 6 and 9.

ARTIFICIAL HORIZON AND DIRECTIONAL GYRO

Too heavy for general use on gliders, the Sperry Artificial Horizon and Directional Gyro could be most useful for instrument flying in clouds. The horizon is a gyroscopic fore and aft and lateral level indicator, and the directional gyro is a direction indicator which is not subject to the unsteadiness of a magnetic compass.

THERMOMETER

A thermometer, although usually thought of as a meteorological research instrument, is of real value to the glider pilot attempting cross-country trips. Abrupt changes in temperature indications give warning of passage from one air mass to another, and even slow changes in indication may provide useful data.

HYGROMETER

For meteorological research work, a hygrometer is also carried. This instrument records relative humidity of the air.

A recommended grouping of the essential instruments is shown in Fig. 12. An arrangement including the Cobb-Slater variometer is pictured in Fig. 13.

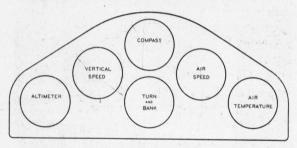

FIG. 12. INSTRUMENT BOARD GROUPING

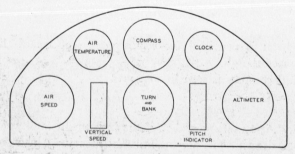

FIG. 13. INSTRUMENT BOARD GROUPING

BAROGRAPH

The barograph is a recording altimeter required on soaring flights for record attempts or contests. In place of the hand of the regular altimeter, the barograph has a stylus the point of which touches a rotating, clockwork-driven drum. This drum has a sheet of tin or aluminum foil wrapped around it and covered with black soot from a flame of burning camphor. When the point of the stylus is moved against the drum in the operating position it cuts a line into the blackening, thus recording the altitude throughout the flight. Properly sealed by an official, this trace or barogram is the required definite proof that a sailplane has been aloft every minute of a cross-country flight. Calibrated before the flight and checked afterward, it provides an accurate record of the maximum altitude achieved on a height record attempt. The duration of a flight also can be measured. A barograph with a drum rotating once every hour and a range from sea level up to 20,000 feet is most satisfactory.

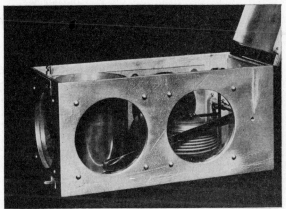

Photo by Boecker

FIG. 14. THE FEIBER BAROGRAPH

Harrisburg Telegraph

FIG. 15. TWO BAROGRAPHS CARRIED ON DISTANCE FLIGHT IN 1935

(Barogram of one on left reproduced on page 173.)

The first barograph developed in the United States specifically for glider work is the Feiber Barograph, shown in Fig. 14. Its one-hour rotation allows careful study of the flight trace. It is of light-weight aluminum construction with large pyralin windows to permit reading of the barogram without opening the case. A convenient locking device allows quick sealing at one point.

Some barographs have been designed for meteorological research. In addition to recording altitude they have another stylus drawing a record of temperature and are called "thermo-barographs." A third stylus is connected with an electric circuit powered by dry batteries and actuated from a button by the pilot when he wishes to record the time of something of interest he has observed during the flight.

CHAPTER VIII

FLIGHT TRAINING

By Lewin B. Barringer

In introducing a student to primary gliding it is well to show him first the parts of the glider and their functions. At the same time he should be taught to make the daily "line" inspection. (See Chapter IV.) By watching the movement of the various controls he has an opportunity to obtain an understanding of their action which will be helpful in mastering their use.

The next step is for the student to seat himself in the cockpit and fasten the safety belt snugly. The importance of fastening the belt should be impressed on him so that he will form early the habit of doing so as his first action on seating himself in any aircraft. It will give him a feeling of security, a "oneness" with the glider, and may prevent serious injury in case of accident.

Placing his feet on the rudder bar or pedals, as the case may be, the student is taught how to steer. With right foot forward he can look back and see the rudder moved to that side. It is well to point out that its action in the air is the same as that of a boat rudder in the water. If his winter sports have included much sledding, he must learn that this steering is exactly opposite. To turn to the right: right foot forward. To turn to the left: left foot forward. This soon seems very natural.

Equally natural is the use of the stick for lateral and longitudinal control. When you look to the right you are likely to incline your head that way. So you move your stick to the right to bank to the right. When you look up or down you pull your head back or bend it forward which corresponds to the action of the control stick in climbing or diving. Another way to place its action in your mind is to try to think of it as being rigidly fastened in its socket. When the left wing drops you move the stick to the right to bring it back up as if you had twisted the whole glider around that way.

As the student moves the controls to learn their use, he can begin another valuable habit, and that is, after fastening the safety belt, always to move the controls as far as they will go in all directions before taking off. This will show whether they are unobstructed and moving freely, which of course is essential to safe operation. Later on he will also check the operation of the brake and the release, but it is better not to confuse his mind with too many details at first.

Before making any tows, it is advisable to let the student learn the use of the stick by sitting in the cockpit with safety belt fastened and balancing the stationary glider in a steady breeze of 15 to 20 m.p.h. To prevent the glider's blowing over it is advisable to tie the nose to a stake with 5 or 6 feet of rope if the wind is strong or gusty. If the glider is balanced on its wheel it is possible even to feel some response to the rudder as it twists the ship slightly from side to side in a strong wind. A glider should never be left faced into a strong wind unless it is well staked down or someone is seated in the cockpit. There should be no obstructions, not even persons standing in front of the glider, as this disturbs the airflow and interferes with the action of the control. The student here can be taught to look straight ahead at the horizon and watch it for keeping his wings level instead of looking sideways at the wing tips. One or two 15-minute periods of this practice is usually sufficient as a preliminary to ground tows.

Although other methods of towing have been used with success for primary training in single-seater gliders, the automobile tow method is by far the safest and most practical where large, level fields are available, so it alone will be described in detail for the first instructions. With it an experienced instructor can have real control over his student and prevent him from getting into trouble.

The equipment needed includes a sturdy car with good power and pick-up and a 150-foot rope. The car should be a roadster or other open type. Full visibility is very important; a closed car with fixed top should never be used. On the rear end of the car there should be an approved type of release such as the DLV. Fastened to this tripping mechanism should be a cord or light piece of rope which at all times should be close beside or in the instructor's hand.

First tows across a level field or airport should be made in a calm or into a wind of not over 5 m.p.h., such conditions usually being found in the early morning or late afternoon. In primary instruction in a single-seater glider it is advisable to have the stick secured forward so that it cannot be pulled back past neutral. This check is best made of stranded control cable with a turnbuckle for adjustment. At first, it is best to check the elevators so that a full backward pull on the stick will bring them only to a point just below neutral. The turnbuckle is then made safe with wire to assure this adjustment remaining constant.

The purpose of this check is to prevent the glider's lifting into the air either from a sudden gust of wind or from too much towing speed during the first tows across the airport. It also gives the student confidence in knowing that he cannot get into trouble if he makes a mistake. The stick should then be held as far back as it can go—not pulled hard back, but held neutral in this position.

Before making the first tow, the student makes sure that his safety belt is fastened, his feet are squarely on the rudder bar and his right hand is holding the stick centered. The instructor makes sure the rings at the two ends of the 150-foot rope are properly fastened in the release mechanism on the glider and on the tow car. He keeps the car in low or second gear and his hand on the release rope.

If a third person is available, it is helpful to have him run along and hold the wing level until the glider has sufficient air speed for lateral control. If not, the student must start off with his stick held all the way to the side of the high wing. He is told to look straight ahead only and to concentrate on keeping the wings level and the glider straight behind the car. His grip on the top of the stick should be firm but relaxed.

The usual fault of most beginners is to overcontrol the rudder. When the glider swerves to one side of the car, the student should push the rudder in the opposite direction but should be ready to bring it back to neutral as soon as the glider is once again in line behind the car. Failure to do this in time will cause the glider to swing to the opposite side. The usual result of attempting to correct this by overcontrolling the rudder will result in zigzagging across the field. This in turn will exert tipping forces on the glider which will make it difficult to keep the wings level. Remember, when the glider has swung too far to the left, push right rudder until it is once again in line, then push enough left rudder to keep it there. There is always this double action—movement of the control to change direction and reverse movement to hold it in the desired course.

The same applies to learning aileron control for balancing the wings. As the student looks straight ahead and feels himself lean to the left as the left wing drops, he must push the stick to the right, all the way if necessary, until he feels the wing come up. As soon as he feels himself once again sitting level he must move the stick back to the left to hold that position and prevent the right wing dropping. It is very helpful for the student to keep checking himself to make sure that his right hand holding the stick is relaxed and that his grip is a light one allowing him to feel what is going on. You do not need any appreciable degree of physical force to fly, but you must have a sensitive feel and good coordination.

This coordination of eyes, sense of balance, and muscular control soon comes with practice. Despite repeated verbal directions from the instructor, the student's grasp of flying is largely self-taught and therefore never leaves him. Learning directional control with the rudder and lateral control with the ailerons may require many tows up and down the field with frequent stops when the zigzags or wing bangings become too severe. The instructor should be patient and must be ready at all times to trip the release which may prevent damage to a wing tip when the student has swerved sharply one way and the resultant slack in the towrope suddenly has been taken up causing the glider to swing quickly in the opposite direction. Learning to fly this way can find a parallel in learning to swim. Despite continuous effort to stay afloat you keep sinking until suddenly you find that you can stay up with no effort and don't know quite how you learned to do it. Similarly the gliding student finds that he can keep the glider straight and level with very little effort.

When the instructor has satisfied himself that the student really has caught on to these two controls by making several tows he can increase the speed of the car until the wings of the glider are just lifting its weight. With the average primary or utility glider this is at an airspeed of about 23 m.p.h., so if, for instance, the towing is being done into a wind of 8 m.p.h., the car should be driven at 15-20 m.p.h. A slight readjustment of the cable check on the control stick may be necessary to allow the glider to skim off the ground a few inches.

With this first leaving of the ground, the student begins to experience the great thrill of motorless flying. The bumping across the field becomes less and less as the wings gradually take up the load and the craft becomes airborne. With this increase in speed there is also increase of control so the student will find it less effort to keep straight and level. The importance of keeping the wings level when in flight close to the ground should be emphasized.

As the student becomes more at home in controlling the glider, the instructor can loose the check still more and allow flights up to 2 or 3 feet. With the check still on there is a possibility of danger in climbing too high as the student might push the stick too far forward causing the glider to dive and then not have sufficient control to level out before hitting the ground. For this reason it is advisable to undo the check entirely as soon as the student has shown sufficient aptitude. If the student should pull back too far or be lifted suddenly to 10 feet or more by a gust and continues to hold the stick back while the check is still on, the instructor can allow the glider to settle to the ground by gradually decreasing the speed of the tow car.

As he skims a few feet off the ground, the student can turn most of his attention to mastering the fore and aft movement of the stick as he now keeps straight and level almost instinctively. The best way to attain an equal proficiency in elevator control is to pull back gently when the glider has sufficient flying speed, climb to a height of 5 feet and then concentrate on trying to hold that elevation without touching the ground or climbing higher while being towed the length of a long field. At the start the student must be cautioned never to take off until he is sure that his wings are level and his course is straight behind the car.

It is well for the instructor to give a hand signal when he is about to slow down at the end of the field so that the student can nose down slightly and land. The correct procedure in landing is to pull back gently just a little on the stick when a few inches off the ground so that the wheel or central part of the wooden skid touches first. In landing, the student must be taught to look from 100 to 300 feet ahead so as to be able accurately to judge his height above the ground. If he looks down directly in front of him he sees the ground rushing by and cannot form an accurate judgment of elevation.

After 8 or 10 tows where consistently level heights of around 5 feet are maintained and good landings made, the average student is ready to go higher and make his first free flight. The best way to instruct him in this is to tell him to climb to about 15-20 feet and prepare to release when the instructor signals him down with his hand. He should be warned not to hurry but to nose down a bit and then pull the release ring. Before this flight and on all subsequent flights, he should keep his left hand on the release at all times while being towed. After releasing he should glide down, keeping steady flying speed until the slight leveling out to land. This speed he can judge best by the amount of wind on his face and the "solid" feel of the controls. For primary instruction this is preferable to the use of an airspeed indicator which may become inaccurate from being clogged by grass seeds, dirt or moisture while towing over the ground. It is better at first to develop a sense of flying "feel" rather than a dependence on instruments.

After his first free glide, which constitutes his second real milestone and thrill of his gliding career, the student can be allowed to make higher and higher tows until he has reached the maximum possible with the 150-foot rope. This is about 120 feet and seems almost directly over the tow car. From this height the first shallow turns can be taught. This is the most critical stage in gliding instruction where the advantages of two-seater training become most apparent. Lacking this equipment, instructions with a single seater should be given with great care.

The student should be told about the causes and dangers of stalling as a result of insufficient flying speed and how easy it is to stall and fall off in a turn which requires slightly more flying speed than straight flying. The first turns should be made from a height of about 100 feet and should be only 15°-20°. If there is any wind, it is advisable to tow slightly crosswind so that the landings are made directly into the wind. The student should be cautioned not to pull the stick back causing the glider to stall nor to push it forward causing it to dive as he moves it to one side to bank. In the average, well designed glider only a slight amount of rudder is needed in the direction of the turn. It is wise to have him make each maneuver separately: get sufficient flying speed on the ground, take off, climb, nose down slightly, release, steady flight at proper speed for a moment, turn, level out, land. In turning one should always lead off with the stick to bank, followed immediately by the rudder. Too much bank for a given radius of turn will result in a slip. Too much rudder will result in a sideways skid and possible stall. All turns should be completed at least 20 feet above the ground so that there never will be the danger of a wing tip touching the ground while the glider is in flight.

From the first gradual turns right and left he progresses to 90° and finally 180° turns with the 150-foot rope. Greater towline lengths may be preferable for two-seater instruction or on exceptionally large fields. Although first turns should be made in a calm or with a slight breeze, it is advisable to have well advanced students become accustomed to turning in winds of up to 20 m.p.h. Downwind landings should not be attempted in such strong winds, however. In making 90° and 180° turns the instructor should take care to give the student as much room as possible with regard to obstructions bordering the flying field. At first he should signal when to release, but later he should tell the student to use his own judgment. If the glider is equipped with a brake the student should keep his hand on it when landing. If he is overshooting and in danger of colliding with a fence or other obstruction he must pull on the brake and push the stick hard forward. Unless he is landing on wet grass, this will bring the glider to a quick stop.

After the student can make consistently good 180° turns in

either direction, he is ready for higher tows with a longer rope. The student should be cautioned on all high tows not to pull up steeply until over 200 feet high so as to have sufficient altitude to recover in the event of the rope breaking. With the 500-foot length the student can climb to approximately 400 feet which is ample to make a 360° turn and landing in the center of the field. The best way to instruct him to do this is to tell him to make a 180° turn after releasing, fly downwind over one side of the field to the other end and then make another 180° turn in the same direction and come in for a landing in the center of the field.

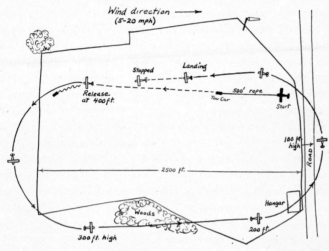

A 360° Turn to the Left

He must be cautioned to use his judgment in deciding when to turn so that he will not overshoot or undershoot the field. There is danger of the former during good thermal conditions which may prolong the flight. It is well under such conditions for the instructor to make a 360° flight first both to determine the advisability of letting the student try it at that time and to show him how he should do it. If he should undershoot slightly and run into danger of not quite getting over the fence or other obstruction he should be told to dive toward the bottom of it and then pull over it rather than stretching his glide which may cause him to stall down on top of it.

After he has made several of these flights in either direction he can try a figure eight, making the first 180° turn in one direction and the second in the opposite direction. Soon the handling of the glider in the air will become quite natural and the student can use his own judgment about when to turn and can concentrate on making precision landings. With a little practice he should be able to land and stop without the use of the brake within 100 and later within 50 feet of the airport circle or other designated mark.

Between lessons, especially if they are spaced far apart, a student should be required to "check out" by going through the preliminary stages of ground skimming and straight flights from low altitude to demonstrate his ability to progress further that day.

At this stage it is well to demonstrate a forward slip and slight fishtailing, the former for losing height without increase of speed and the latter for reducing excess speed close to the ground. A slip is a valuable maneuver for losing height at a steep angle after misjudging or coming in too high purposely to be sure to clear obstructions. By banking to the left and applying right rudder, the fuselage is skidded sideways exerting considerable drag without impairing the lift of the wings. Naturally this maneuver is useless with a primary glider which has no side keel area to make the necessary resistance. Fishtailing is kicking the rudder hard from side to side while keeping the wings level. Again, these maneuvers best can be taught first in a two-place, dual-control glider.

It will be of great assistance throughout the course of training to have the instructor demonstrate all the various maneuvers. It is also helpful to have a class of several students with some of those who are not flying riding in the tow car and others watching from the sidelines trying to analyze the mistakes of the student in the glider.

Where fields are too small or sloping to permit automobile towing, successful training has been done by the shock-cord or "bungee" method. An outstanding club where initial training is done entirely by this means followed by winch towing is the London Gliding Club. Short "slides" followed by skimming flights are given to the students after the same introduction of balancing the stationary glider in a winch that precedes automobile towing.

Using the general procedure of shock-cord towing outlined in Chapter V, the power of the first tows is greatly reduced by less man power and shorter stretch of the rubber rope so that upon release the glider at first does not leave the ground but has sufficient speed to permit lateral control for a short distance. With this system the student is instructed at first to keep his rudder centered with the foot bar straight across for the first few skimming flights.

It is impossible to give exact details for this type of towing due to the slope and surface friction of the ground, the life and consequent elasticity of the shock cord, the pull of the towing crew, and the force of the wind, which are all variable factors. The instructor should use the general information about automobile tow and shock-cord launchings and proceed cautiously so that an inexperienced student will not be catapulted into the air until he has had sufficient ground slides and skimming flights.

PRIMARY SOARING INSTRUCTION

For the most part, glider pilots have made their first sustained flights and won their "C" licenses for 5-minute flights above point of release over a slope soaring site. This is the easiest type of soaring, still most commonly done. If possible it should be preceded by instruction in a two-seater glider or in a light airplane teaching stalls and spins and recovery therefrom.

For slope soaring one usually must have a steep ridge of 45° or more and several hundred feet high facing the wind with safe landing areas on top or bottom, preferably both. If taking off on top of the ridge from a field 800 or more feet long winch towing is preferable. If the field is too small for winch or auto tow either hand or auto shock cord must be used. This latter launching should never be used for a student making his first soaring flight unless he has had plenty of practice with it on a large, level field. He should also have had winch towing practice if a winch is used. A utility type glider equipped with airspeed indicator, variometer and altimeter is proper for preliminary soaring. A wind of 15-20 m.p.h. is usually preferable for first slope soaring.

After releasing from the launching he should fly straight out until he is in the area of rising air in front of the slope. This he usually will feel, but also can notice by the variometer needle moving up, indicating that the glider is climbing. He must be cautioned not to pull up the nose of the glider when encountering the lift as this may cause a stall and in any case increase the glider's sinking speed. Instead he should fly at a steady speed a few miles per hour faster than normal gliding in quiet air over an airport. This will mean about 30 m.p.h. for the average utility glider. The added speed is for better control, as some turbulence may be encountered.

As soon as his glider is in the area of rising air the student should turn in the direction that will allow him the longest straight flight before reaching the end of the ridge. When he does come near this point he should make a 180° turn into the wind *away from the ridge* and continue parallel to the ridge down to the other end where he will turn in the opposite direction, again into the wind and away from the ridge. While flying a course parallel to the ridge the glider will be pointed sideways into the wind, that is, it will be "crabbing" sideways to hold this course while flying crosswind.

As a result its ground speed is often very slow. It is possible that he soon will rise to a height of 500 to 1000 feet above the ridge where the air will be smoother and the area of lift wider. After half an hour he should fly out over the valley away from the area of lift and glide down to a landing in a designated field. If he stays up longer than this he is apt to become overtired which will affect his judgment adversely. It is advisable before a student's first soaring flight to have the instructor make a flight first showing just how it should be done.

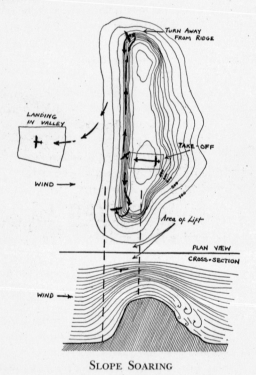

SLOPE SOARING

Although in the past slope soaring has nearly always preceded thermal soaring, the latter, which offers far greater possibilities for real performances, is being used more and more to obtain primary soaring experience. The reason for this is that many gliding clubs now exist in level country far from any mountains. Before trying this type of soaring it is even more important, if possible, to have dual, two-seater glider or lightplane instruction. It is necessary to learn, in addition to stalls and spins, how to make a continuous turn or spiral of comparatively narrow diameter. This can well be taught at a reasonably high altitude of several thousand feet by gliding down in a two-seater glider after releasing from airplane tow or gliding down in a lightplane with the engine throttled. The instructor should teach a student how to make turns where the glider is banked more than 45° and the elevator and rudder controls become reversed.

For first thermal soaring over level country it is advisable to have a large field, allowing winch or auto towing for at least 4000 feet. This will make possible heights of 800 feet or more. Most thermal "bubbles" are comparatively narrow and weak at low altitudes and can rarely be used to climb when encountered below 500 feet, especially by an inexperienced pilot. Convection, or thermal activity, is best in the summer months and rarely is strong enough for soaring before ten o'clock in the morning.

ELIOT F. NOYES, BOSTON ARCHITECT, LANDS AFTER FIVE-HOUR FLIGHT OVER SLEEPING BEAR DUNE, ONE WEEK AFTER HIS FIRST FLYING INSTRUCTIONS

As in other phases of training it is best for the instructor to make a flight to show the student how it should be done. If he is familiar with the local conditions he probably will know where thermals usually start. It may take the student a number of tows before he encounters one of these invisible bubbles of rising air. When he does, usually he will feel a slight turbulence. However, this is not always so and in any case he should pay close attention to his variometer and air speed.

Sometimes he may glide into a weak thermal which will bring the variometer reading up from the normal glide of — 3 feet per second to the zero mark. This means that the thermal is rising at 3 feet per second, so by spiraling to stay within it the glider just maintains altitude. One of the author's students encountered such a condition after releasing at 700 feet and by careful spiraling managed to stay up 15 minutes on his "C" flight although he rose only slightly above this height. Others have climbed several thousand feet on their first thermals. While spiraling in thermals it is well to keep an eye on the position of the glider with respect to the landing field as the thermal acts very much like a balloon and will drift with the wind. It may be necessary to leave it to be sure to be able to glide back to the field. Wind is not always present on days of good thermal activity.

CHAPTER IX

SOARING TECHNIQUE

By Lewin B. Barringer

SOARING FLIGHT CAN BE DIVIDED into three principal categories: endurance, distance and altitude. Of the three, endurance soaring is the least important.

It is the aim of every experienced soaring pilot continually to improve his knowledge and skill until he is able to make record performances. A new record with its attendant publicity is always a help to the progress of motorless flight and this is the chief value of endurance soaring, which otherwise is only a "glorified form of flagpole sitting" proving nothing more than the constancy of the wind and the physical endurance of the pilot.

Without exception all endurance soaring records have been made over slope soaring sites. Most of them have been made over sand dunes on steady sea breezes. From the time a pilot makes his first half hour soaring flight he soon progresses to flights of 2 and 3 hours. His first endurance goal is the 5-hour requirement for the "Silver C" license. Beyond that he has to look for incentive to set new state, national and international records. Many states have yet to have a record established but both the United States and the world records are now so high that any attempt to better them will involve night flying. These records are divided into two categories for single- and multi-seater gliders.

Before a pilot attempts an endurance flight of even so much as 12 hours he must be in excellent physical condition and should make flights of 7 or 10 hours which will teach him many things that are essential to the success of later record attempts. First of these is that he must be adequately clothed. Sufficient warmth is even more important than a comfortable, well-padded seat. He should carry a supply of food and drink. Experience on several long flights has taught us the value of eating something such as a chocolate bar or cookies every hour to keep up energy. Oranges are valuable as thirst quenchers. If a flight is continued on into or through the night hours it is wise to have a thermos of hot coffee or other stimulant to help keep awake. Caffein pills may also help, but these should be used with care. Of great importance are sanitary considerations. On any flight of more than an hour's duration, especially in cold weather, the pilot should carry an empty bottle with wide neck and with watertight screw cap. In a flight of 5 hours or longer this is an absolute necessity, because a full bladder can cause extreme physical discomfort affecting flying skill and judgment. There is the very real danger of a possible hard landing, or crack-up, when a sudden blow easily can cause a full bladder to burst with fatal results. Although it is not generally known, many deaths have resulted because of this condition from automobile and airplane accidents which otherwise would not have caused serious injury.

Any night soaring should be preceded by a number of hours of instruction in night and instrument flying in airplanes. Unless a pilot has this experience he may get into serious trouble as he probably will find that he cannot adjust his judgment on his first night flight, unless, of course, there is bright moonlight. Even if this is so, thick clouds may cut off all light so that he will have to rely entirely on his instruments to maintain level flight.

These must include an airspeed indicator, variometer, altimeter, and turn and bank indicator. A clinometer, compass and clock are also useful. All instruments should be illuminated by radiolite figures and pointers or by indirect lighting, preferably controlled by a rheostat. If available, a 5-meter transceiver radio set can be of real value on such a flight. To comply with government regulations, navigation lights must be carried: a green light on the right wing tip, a red light on the left wing tip, and a white light on the tail.

For any night endurance soaring attempt there should be a number of guiding lights spaced as evenly as possible outlining the top and bottom of the ridge. In addition, the landing field or area should be outlined with small lights such as lanterns. If any floodlights are available, they should be used with care as they are apt to blind the pilot. As for all other soaring record attempts, the glider must carry a barograph installed and sealed by the qualified official who witnesses the take-off and landing.

Certainly one of the most important considerations is the choice of a site for the record attempt. Some of the best places in America are the sand dunes in the vicinity of Frankfort, Michigan, which offer almost unlimited facilities for landing on the beaches. Even on the darkest night it usually is possible to see the glimmer marking the surf and to land alongside it.

The question of air traffic with two or more gliders slope soaring over the same ridge is a serious one, especially if the ridge is limited in extent. Before a number of pilots take off for soaring on the same ridge they should all agree to definite traffic rules to lessen the ever-present danger of collision. In passing a glider coming in the opposite direction it usually is best to keep to the right. In overtaking another glider flying at the same altitude it is best to stay on the side closest to the ridge where the lift is strongest. If flying at approximately the same altitude as several other ships, it is most important to follow the rule of always turning away from the ridge. There have been head-on collisions between two gliders where one pilot turned suddenly in the opposite direction to that expected by the pilot following close behind him.

Endurance soaring for new records had best be done in the two-seater category, as demonstrated by the last two international records. It is doubtful if the present mark, a flight of more than two days and nights, could have been made solo. With two pilots relieving each other in shifts, the chances of making a new record are greatly increased without the danger of the pilot falling asleep.

The greatest value to be derived from endurance soaring over ridges, aside from record setting, is the building up of general flying experience. Hours spent in the air piloting under any sort of condition can be of value in building up the combination of skill and confidence needed by a good all-around pilot. While making endurance flights a pilot can best prepare himself for the more important types of soaring flight by perfecting his turns and generally concentrating on making all his flying smooth and effortless.

DISTANCE SOARING

Although it is possible to use a secondary or utility glider for establishing endurance records by slope soaring, an intermediate or, preferably, a high performance type is needed for long distance or high altitude soaring on thermal upcurrents. Before attempting a cross-country flight with one of these sailplanes a pilot should first make a number of flights to familiarize himself with his ship and feel at home in it. In getting used to it he should practice enough landings to a mark in varying atmospheric conditions so that he can land safely in a small field if need be.

The easiest way first to practice the thermal soaring technique essential for either distance or altitude soaring is from airplane tow. By this method the instructor piloting the airplane can tow his student in the sailplane to an altiude of 3000 feet or more where the thermal upcurrents are wider and stronger than they are closer to the ground. With a sensitive variometer installed in the airplane the instructor can tell when he is in rising air and signal to the student just when to release. Probably even before releasing the student will notice his variometer needle registering the fact that the sailplane is rising. To stay within the invisible boundaries of the rising bubble or column of warmer air he must immediately bank his sailplane and begin a steady turn or spiral.

The ability to make smooth, continuous spirals is the most important single accomplishment in advanced soaring flight. In making shallow turns of consequently rather large diameter the pilot keeps his nose far enough down to fly 4 or 5 m.p.h. above stalling speed,

CORRECT

STRAIGHT – LEVEL   SHALLOW LEFT TURN   STEEP LEFT TURN

INCORRECT

STRAIGHT-LEFT WING LOW   LEFT TURN – SLIPPING   LEFT TURN – SKIDDING

VARIOUS FLIGHT ATTITUDES AS SHOWN BY THE TURN AND BANK INDICATOR

leads off with his stick banking the sailplane and immediately follows with enough rudder to hold the ship in the turn. He then holds his controls so that he continues to turn, being careful to coordinate his stick and rudder so that the ball of the ball bank will remain centered at all times. If he has too much bank or too little rudder for a given left turn the ball will roll to the left indicating that he is slipping down out of the turn. To correct this he should move the stick to the right to reduce the bank or push his left foot farther forward to apply more rudder until the ball is again centered. As he becomes more experienced he usually will use a combination of the two controls to smooth out his turns. As thermal upcurrents are often quite turbulent he must be constantly on the alert to keep flying as smoothly as possible.

In the event that thermal soaring is being done without a ball bank in an open cockpit sailplane the pilot must rely on his sense of feel while watching the variometer. If he has too little bank or too much rudder for a given left turn he will feel a blast of air on his right cheek indicating he is skidding out of the turn. If equipped with a ball bank this will be shown by the ball rolling to the right. Correction is made by steepening the bank or reducing the rudder until the ball is centered again. A good rule to remember for open cockpit flying without the ball bank is to correct by pushing rudder on the side you feel the blast of excess slipstream indicating that you are skidding or slipping.

After becoming proficient in making smooth, shallow spirals the student should practice the steep turns often necessary for climbing in thermals of narrow diameter or staying in the center of large thermals where the lift is strongest. As this requires more skill and can more easily get the student into trouble, it should first be practiced at a reasonably high altitude of over 1000 feet. If airplane tow or high winch launchings are not available for practice flights it is wise to get some steep turn instructions in a light airplane. Dual instruction in a two-seater sailplane released from airplane tow is the ideal method.

Before making steep spiral turns it is well first to have an understanding of the forces involved. In speaking of steep turns we consider those where the wings of the sailplane are banked at an angle of more than 45° with respect to the horizon.

In making a turn a glider produces a centrifugal force which tends to force it out of the turn. The shorter the radius of turn, the stronger this outward pull becomes. For a correct turn the angle of bank must be so that the component or the result of the combined pull of gravity downward and centrifugal force outward exerts a pressure vertically to the wings, holding the glider in the turn. The pilot must use the correct amount of bank for a given radius and air speed to make a proper steep turn or continuous spiral.

In steep turns the action of the controls becomes reversed so that the elevators hold the sailplane in the turn and the rudder is now used to keep the nose of the sailplane in the correct attitude with respect to the horizon. In starting a steep spiral it is best to nose down to a speed 5 to 10 m.p.h. in excess of normal cruising speed and then bank gradually but steadily until the desired angle is reached, using as little rudder as possible. As the ship banks beyond 45° the stick must be pulled back sufficiently to hold the turn and keep the ball centered. If it is not pulled back hard enough the sailplane will slip down steeply sideways. At the same time as the stick is pulled back and held in a position where the desired degree of bank is held constant, the pilot must watch the relation of the nose of the sailplane to the horizon and, if it starts to drop, hold top rudder to keep it up. In a steep left bank this will mean pushing the right rudder pedal.

In learning to master tight spiraling it is easy for the student to stall the sailplane and fall out of control. If too much rudder is used at the beginning of the turn a skid will result which may cause a stall. If he is on his toes and is sensitive to the feeling of sloppy controls when a ship stalls he will be able to recover before a spin develops by straightening out and nosing down until flying speed is regained.

A common mistake of students making tight spirals is to pull back too hard on the stick and either forget about the rudder or apply rudder on the down side. The usual result is a sudden stall followed by a fast spin as the nose drops. It may sometimes take as much as 200 feet to recover, so it is obvious that a beginner should never make steep turns at low altitudes.

Another common cause of stalling and falling off is pulling the stick back too soon at the beginning of a turn. This will cause the air speed to drop close to the stalling point before the turn is well started and the additional drag on the turn will bring about the complete stall.

A complete understanding of stalls and recovery therefrom is essential before any attempt at advanced soaring. It is a common thing to have a sailplane stall a number of times during a distance flight due to flying slowly in turbulent air. A gradual stall in straight-away flight in the average, well designed sailplane first makes itself known to the pilot by the sloppy feeling of the controls. The stick can be moved some way before there is any feeling of response, which is then quite sluggish. If the pilot is experienced he will immediately push the stick forward and regain full flying speed.

If the stall is abrupt from overcontrolling, a badly executed turn, or turbulent air, the sailplane may fall off into a spin in which the nose is down at a steep angle and the whole ship rotating as it falls with the tail making a turn of larger radius than the nose. A well designed ship will come out of a spin after not more than two turns if the pilot takes hands and feet off the controls. It will then fall quickly into a nose dive in which the flying speed and control are regained. Usually it is possible to recover from a spin faster than this by centering the stick and kicking rudder in the direction opposite to the spin which will quickly stop the rotation. As flying speed is regained in the resulting dive the pilot pulls the stick gently back to raise the nose to the normal gliding attitude.

A type of stall that is apt to be disconcerting to a beginner sometimes occurs in thermal soaring where, due to the large wing span of the sailplane, one wing may sweep out of a thermal into a down draft while the other remains in the rising air. This may cause the high wing out of the thermal to stall, resulting in the sailplane falling off in that direction despite an indicated air speed well in excess of a stall.

In preparing for a cross-country soaring flight a pilot must equip himself just as for an endurance flight, with a few additions. He should have a parachute, preferably a back pack for convenience and comfort. His seat should be equipped with an air cushion or other suitable padding and he should have sufficient clothing. On a day when it may be too hot for more than shirt sleeves on the ground it will seem quite cold at 5000 feet. A white cap with sun visor will prevent danger of sunstroke. Other considerations as to food and comfort are the same as outlined for endurance soaring, as a distance flight may easily last more than 5 hours. His instruments should include one or two variometers, an airspeed indicator, ball bank, altimeter, compass and barograph.

A soaring pilot's first cross-country flight may be an attempt to qualify for the 32-mile distance requirement of the "Silver C" license. Before making any flight of this or greater distance, he should study carefully the features of the terrain to be flown over so as to know what to expect both to avoid dangerous areas and to be able to navigate properly. Aerial navigation is a subject the full explanation of which has taken entire books the size of this one, but the navigational problems of the sailplane pilot are not very complex. However, although they are comparatively easy to explain, they may take some time for the student to master unless he has an exceptionally fine sense of direction and orientation.

First of all he must have a good aerial map showing such features as towns, mountains, rivers, lakes, railroads, and principal highways. The best maps for this purpose are the Sectional Airway Maps printed by the Civil Aeronautics Authority in Washington, D. C. These have a scale of 8 miles to the inch and 1000 feet contour changes indicated by different shadings of color. All unnecessary and confusing details have been omitted and the important essentials made very clear. Lacking one or more of these maps, the best of road maps, such as those distributed by the Esso Touring Service, may be quite adequate, especially if the pilot has no definite destination and wishes simply to fly straight down wind as far as possible. The chief disadvantage of these maps is that they do not include the railroads.

Before taking off the pilot should check his wind direction and draw a line on his map indicating his probable course straight down wind. It is helpful to mark 10-mile intervals along this line so that he will be able to check his progress cross country. Also marked along the line should be the compass heading he wishes to fly. This can be found easily by laying a transparent protractor calibrated from zero to 360° over the map. The center point should lie on the course line where it intersects a line of latitude or longitude. If one of the former is used the East-West or 90°-270° line of the protractor should exactly coincide with the horizontal line on the map indicating the latitude. The magnetic course can then be read off directly in degrees. This must then be corrected for deviation and variation.

Deviation is a magnetic error caused by attraction of metal parts in the sailplane. As most sailplanes are largely of wood construction this rarely needs to be considered. However, it is well to have the compass compensated and errors, if any, listed on a small card.

Variation is the difference between true North and the magnetic pole. It is indicated on the Airways Maps by dotted red lines listed at the edge as a certain number of degrees plus or minus. Variation West is plus and East is minus. This can be remembered by "West is best and East is least."

If the wind on the day of the cross-country flight is from the northwest, the down wind course will be read off the map at 135°. If there is a deviation error of −2° this is subtracted to make 133°. If the variation in the particular part of the country is 9° West or +9°, the course to be flown is 142°.

Whether a road map is used to navigate in the air or not it is advisable to have one of the area in which the landing will be made and leave a duplicate with your ground crew. This will greatly facilitate letting them know your exact location when telephoning after the landing. It is helpful, too, to write down the number of the telephone at the starting site on the road map carried in the sailplane.

It is best to start from a well tested site where thermal activity is known to be excellent on days of good convection. If this is a place such as the Warren Eaton Site at Elmira, the flight may start with local slope soaring as soon as the wind is of sufficient velocity and blowing up the ridge. This may be as early as eight o'clock, but the thermals are seldom strong enough here to start cross country before nine-thirty or ten o'clock.

When a thermal upcurrent is encountered while slope soaring, its presence is usually indicated by a slight turbulence and a definite rise in the rate of climb as shown by the variometer. Although there may be one or two good cumulus clouds, it is well to wait until more form, indicating steady convection at regular intervals. The start cross country should not be made until the pilot has climbed to the cloud base, which may be from 3000 to 5000 feet. In no case should he start from a ridge site such as Elmira unless he is at least 3000 feet above his take-off. Otherwise the downwash

Antelo Devereux

CUMULUS CLOUDS ON A GOOD DISTANCE SOARING DAY

effect on the lee side of the mountains may cause him to lose so much altitude that he is forced to land after covering only a mile or two.

It is well to consider carefully the adverse effects of downwinds on the lee side of mountain ridges, as they sometimes are very dangerous for any type of aircraft. The author can remember two cases where they almost caused him to crash. One was in Virginia while slope soaring about 500 feet above a 2000-foot ridge. The altitude was 4500 feet above sea level and cumulus clouds were coming by about 1000 feet over the slope. By watching one of these too carefully while endeavoring to catch the thermal forming it, he failed to see that the sailplane was drifting to the lee of a spur of the irregular ridge. Suddenly the variometer registered a very rapid descent of more than 10 feet per second. Only by diving at 65 m.p.h. was he able to clear the ridge by a scant 20 feet and reach the safety of the windward side. On another occasion on a long mountain range in Pennsylvania he was forced to fly to the lee of the ridge as the wind changed sufficiently to render slope soaring precarious over a long belt of unbroken forest. On the downwind side there was a possible landing field. As the sailplane flew toward it at a fairly high speed of 50 m.p.h. to give adequate control, it suddenly was caught in the downdraft so violently that both wing tips flexed sharply and the cockpit cover was torn loose, the wood splitting and the screws pulling out. If the sailplane had not been well designed with adequate reserve strength, it would probably

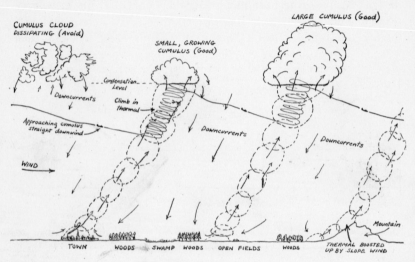

CROSS-COUNTRY SOARING

have broken up in the air by this terrific jolt. It is best always to keep in mind the wind direction and to remember that with sufficient velocity there will always be downdrafts in the lee of ridges and that these are likely to be turbulent and dangerous.

After the first spiral climb to the cloud base the thermal should be left before entering the cloud, especially if the pilot is not experienced in cloud flying and equipped with the necessary instruments. In starting off downwind it is best to increase speed to get through the adjoining downcurrents quickly before much height is lost. After that, in air that is neither rising nor falling it is best to fly at minimum sinking speed to conserve precious altitude. It is often advisable at first to head off at an angle instead of directly downwind where the downcurrents are apt to be strongest. Then a downwind course should be held toward the nearest cumulus cloud that seems to be growing, indicating strong lift beneath it.

Of great importance for any successful cross-country soaring flight is an ability to differentiate between cumulus clouds that are forming and those that have reached their maximum size and are ready to dissipate. Under the former will be found the strong lift of a "live" thermal current. Under the latter will be little if any rising air, and possibly strong downcurrents.

Although it takes considerable practice to be able to choose clouds accurately, there are several indications that are very helpful. A small cumulus cloud that has just begun to form will have the typical "cotton-ball" rounded top effect, almost always with a flat bottom at the condensation level. If watched carefully it will be seen to boil up slowly as it grows and the top of the cloud lifts higher and higher. One of the best indications of the fact that such

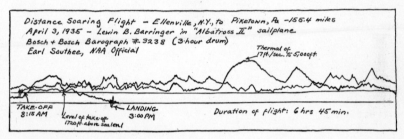

BAROGRAM OF DISTANCE FLIGHT

a cloud is growing are small, wave-like curls that continue to appear on the sides and top of the cloud. If watched these curls will be seen to roll over and be swallowed up by the growing cloud. This manifestation is particularly marked on days of considerable wind velocity when the thermals are quite turbulent and there is a definite rolling movement of the up-currents forming the clouds. Clouds that have passed their maximum and are about to break up are usually characterized by a straggly, ragged appearance of their edges.

Many times during the summer months thermal upcurrents and the cumulus clouds marking them will be so frequent and evenly spaced that even a novice pilot will have little difficulty continuing on his course for many miles. He must remember, however, that no soaring flight is flown on an absolutely straight line as is possible with powered flight. There is a continual zigzagging to utilize the best lift. On some flights made by the author it was necessary to make a wide detour 10 miles to one side of the course to follow a line of clouds that looked promising when the air straight ahead had been quite empty of any clouds.

Sometimes it is advisable to follow a rather wide zigzag course if there is a possibility of encountering the regular parallel bands of thermals forming the horizontal rolls which cause what we call "cloud streets." Typical cloud streets that appear frequently over level farm lands can be recognized easily from the ground as long rows of cumulus clouds practically touching and running parallel straight downwind. As this condition is not always so easy to recognize in flight, a varied course may be necessary to disclose its

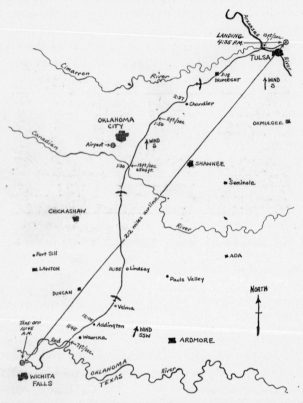

SKETCH MAP OF THE AUTHOR'S 212-MILE GOAL FLIGHT, APRIL 19, 1938

presence. A well developed cloud street is the greatest possible help on a distance flight, as on one side of the line of clouds there is practically unbroken lift, making it possible to fly straight for some time without spiraling and often at fairly high speed.

On the opposite side of continuous lift of a cloud street there is the down part of the roll which causes a "waterfall" of air as continuous as the rising air on the other side, and of course this should be avoided. Eric Nessler, writing of his French distance record made in the spring of 1938, described flying a considerable distance on the upside of a horizontal roll unmarked by any clouds.

On the author's record distance flight in Texas he twice encountered for about 20 miles a line of clouds so close as to be almost touching and looking just like a cloud street, but which proved not to be a continuous horizontal roll as he found downcurrents between each two clouds. However, the areas of lift were so wide and the downdrafts so narrow that it was possible to fly straight for some time. The technique used was to fly slowly enough to get maximum lift under one cloud without spiraling and then fly quite rapidly

Wichita Daily Times Photo

AFTER BREAKING THE AMERICAN DISTANCE RECORD

L. to R.—Leon Bonotaux (crew), Karl O. Lange (with barograph), the author, Harland Ross, James Kimbrell (pilot of tow plane), Kenneth Findiesen (crew).

through the intervening downcurrent to the next where he again slowed up and quickly regained whatever height had been lost.

Strong thermal upcurrents unmarked by any clouds and consequently called "dry thermals" are fairly common in certain parts of the country, especially in the deserts of California, Arizona and New Mexico. It was with such conditions on a cloudless day that John Robinson of San Diego set an unofficial altitude record of 10,200 feet in an intermediate sailplane in 1938. Distance soaring on dry thermals is, of course, harder without the cumulus clouds as markers to point the way.

A great help occasionally are other indications of lift, such as leaves, butterflies, and soaring birds. The latter are sometimes very useful to a soaring pilot. While losing altitude and not knowing which way to turn he may see a buzzard, a hawk or an eagle spiraling nearby and steadily gaining altitude. Soaring birds do not fear sailplanes and sometime seem to welcome these big man-made birds to their element. The author has been able to fly within 10 feet of a golden eagle when both were almost standing still heading into a slopewind. On other occasions he has had large hawks fly straight toward him from some distance to join him in the upcurrent in which they saw him spiraling.

It is interesting that the best modern sailplanes will out-perform most of the soaring birds, with the probable exception of such master soarers as the albatross and the man-o'-war bird, in sinking speed and gliding ratio. However, the birds more than make up for their deficiencies in this respect by their small size, marvelous maneuverability and vastly superior experience. A bird will do more flying in a few months than most pilots in a lifetime; a soaring pilot can always learn by watching them.

A common indication of thermal action in desert country are the common "dust devils" seen more rarely in other parts of the country. These are the cores of thermal columns of rising air. While on an expedition to Iran the author saw on many mornings a large number of these small whirling columns of dust rising from the level plain after ten o'clock in the morning. By noon they sometimes were visible, because of the dust lifted into the air, to heights of over 1000 feet. Nearly everyone has seen a small "dust devil" swirl across a road scattering tumble weeds and dust and then suddenly disappear or seem to stop. This is the taking off of a thermal bubble which starts rotating on the ground before it lifts and starts its upward climb.

In flying straight across country toward a cumulus sloud that is considerably higher than the altitude at which he is cruising, a pilot should approach it straight downwind. The reason for this is that the series of thermal bubbles or the thermal column of rising air leans with the wind. This fact soon becomes apparent even to a beginner as he usually finds when he has climbed several thousand feet in a thermal that he has drifted some distance downwind. The author once experienced an extreme case of drifting with a thermal while on a cross-country flight in Oklahoma. Preparing to land into a high wind when forced down to 350 feet, he encountered a turbulent but weak upcurrent. By careful spiraling, he managed to stay within it to reach a height of only 1500 feet while drifting over 5 miles with the wind.

While flying cross country for real distance on a day of good convection, a pilot should usually not be content to climb on thermals lifting him at 5 feet per second or less. He should continue until he finds lift of 7-10 feet per second registering on his variometer. By regaining altitude on strong thermals much time is saved in utilizing as well as possible the best conditions during the hours when they exist. While in search of such good lift he should not become discouraged when encountering strong downcurrents as these are indications of equally strong upcurrents nearby.

In reaching an area of substantially reduced lift near the top of a thermal (possibly the bottom or trailing part of a thermal bubble) after a rapid climb it is better to straighten out and fly downwind in search of another strong thermal rather than to hang on wasting time while squeezing a last 200 or 300 feet out of this particular upcurrent. However, this does not hold true in the late afternoon when thermal activity is on the decline. Then it is best to get the most out of any rising air that can be found. Wolf Hirth equipped his "Moazagotl" with 100 pounds of water ballast to give him speed while the thermals were strong in the middle of the day. When they weakened around four or five o'clock he dumped the water and partly lowered his flaps while flying slowly to reduce his sinking speed to a minimum and take full advantage of the remaining lift.

If forced low while flying over hilly country it is best to keep a lookout for ridges faced into the wind permitting slope soaring. It is also important before dropping low enough to rely on ridge soaring to check the wind direction by watching cloud shadows, smoke, or ripple marks on water. Often it is possible to find strong thermals by watching the terrain only. If there are light-colored fields in a valley on the windward side of a ridge which has a U-shaped cut-back or ravine the pilot can be almost sure of finding strong thermal lift somewhere to the lee of the top of the ravine. The strongest thermals are those that have risen by convection in the valleys and been given a boost upwards by the mechanical action of the wind being deflected over a mountain.

It is often possible to prolong a flight by slope soaring over a ridge while waiting for a thermal to come along on which to climb to a height sufficient to make it possible to continue cross country. Of course, it is not possible to fall back on this type of soaring when flying over level country, but a careful study of terrain features will often prevent a premature landing. One should look for lift over or to the lee side of light-colored and dry ground and avoid downcurrents over dense woodland, lakes, and swampy ground. Strong thermals sometimes form along medium-sized rivers, a fact the author experienced several times during level country flights in Texas and Oklahoma.

When forced low enough so that a landing is probable, the pilot should decide on a landing field while looking for rising currents to prolong the flight. He may sometimes find it advisable to land rather than to struggle on in a weak thermal when a stretch of several miles of unbroken forest lies ahead. Great wooded areas, such as the Pocono Mountains in Pennsylvania where there are stretches of 20 miles or more without a clearing large enough to land in, should not be crossed unless good thermals are abundant and the pilot is 3000 to 5000 feet high. This area must be crossed on record flight attempts to the south and southeast from Elmira.

When choosing a place in which to land the pilot should first make sure that it is large enough. If there are obstructions about such as high trees, houses, or high tension lines he should keep them well in mind as he notices the wind direction and makes his

TYPICAL END OF A CROSS-COUNTRY FLIGHT
On a farm in Pennsylvania after take-off at Elmira.

approach. It is a good rule to come in purposely somewhat high to make sure of clearing all obstructions. Excess height can then be lost by the use of spoilers, flaps, and slipping. If the speed is high when the sailplane is a few feet above the ground and there is danger of not stopping before reaching the end of the field, the sailplane should be landed, the control stick pushed full forward, and the brake pulled on hard. Unless the surface is covered with ice or wet grass the sailplane can usually be brought to a quick stop in a surprisingly short distance, and with no danger of overturning. At the end of the author's long ridge soaring flight he stopped in 40 feet from a landing at 60 m.p.h., the nose skid digging several inches into the ground without doing any damage.

It is best for the pilot to be prepared to secure the ship in case of a landing in a high wind where there is no one at hand to assist him. In Texas the author carried, in addition to wrench, hammer and pliers to help disassemble the ship, three thin steel stakes with 6 feet of ¼-inch rope tied to them. On one landing in Oklahoma there was a 30-mile wind blowing and no human help within 2 miles. Holding the nose down with his weight as he climbed out and pulled the stakes out of the baggage compartment of the Minimoa, he quickly ducked under the wing and caught the tail before the nose could rise putting the wings in a lifting position. Then, balancing the wings, he walked the tail around and swung the ship until it headed downwind. It was then secured level with ropes to each wing at aileron hinge fittings and to the nose.

In a case like this it is advisable not to tie the ropes so they are taut as this may cause undue strain on the wings. If the ship is left overnight, dew or rain may cause the ropes to shrink and, if not enough slack is left, this may cause a wing spar to crack. Another good rule to remember to save the wings from strain is not to hold a tip rigidly while the sailplane is being towed slowly over uneven ground. Instead, the man at the wing tip should hold his two hands, palms toward each other, horizontally about 6 inches apart, allowing the oscillation of the tip of the wing to have free play between.

After the landing the pilot should reach in and push the plunger on his barograph lifting the stylus from the drum. If his is a record flight he should wait until a responsible witness, preferably a man of some standing in the community, does this for him and signs the blank forms carried on the flight. No record attempt should be made in the United States without these necessary forms obtainable from The Soaring Society of America, P. O. Box 71, Elmira, New York. It is also necessary to have an official glider observer representing the S.S.A. and the National Aeronautic Association to start the barograph and witness the take-off if the flight is for "Silver C" distance or a national or international record. It is a good idea to carry two barographs because of the possible failure of one.

Another means of distance soaring is flying crosswind before a polar or cold front. As explained in Chapter VI, a polar air mass on coming into contact with warmer air of sufficiently great difference in temperature will cause a line of clouds and storms before which the air is rising. If a pilot can find such a condition and can manage to stay out in front of it without being drawn into the storm he should be able to travel a considerable distance. Line storms of this nature have been known to extend along a front over 1000 miles long. This type of distance soaring should be attempted only by an experienced pilot in a modern, completely equipped sailplane. Present will be all the hazards of storm flying described under altitude soaring.

A good idea for cross-country soaring is to have two pilots flying sailplanes of similar performance to keep within sight of one another. This not only adds greatly to the enjoyment of the flight but can be of real help to both pilots. This was proven conclusively on the only "formation" flight yet made by Warren Eaton and the author in the "Falcon" * and the "Albatross II," two Bowlus-du Pont sister ships. In the fall of 1934 they soared together from Big Meadows to Front Royal, Virginia, a distance of 31 miles. It

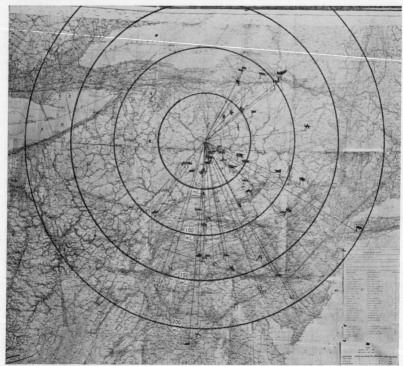

Fred T. Loomis

DISTANCE FLIGHTS FROM ELMIRA DURING 1938 NATIONAL CONTEST

was a particularly difficult flight along a serrated part of the Blue Mountain ridge and was largely possible because it was made with two ships. There were many times when one flew toward the other to take advantage of better lift that he had found.

Another thing for the experienced pilot to add enjoyment to his flight as well as to make a contribution to the art is to carry a pad and frequently jot down notes as to lift, terrain features, types of clouds, temperatures at various altitudes, etc. The author usually has done this with the pad strapped to his right knee with a rubber

* Now in the Smithsonian Museum, Washington, D. C.

band and the pencil slipped under one of the bands when not being used.

GOAL FLIGHT

Only slightly different from those of an ordinary distance flight are the considerations and preparations for a goal flight to a definite destination announced to the officials before the take-off. Accurate navigation is naturally much more important for this type of flight. Although Stanley Corcoran made the third longest flight at that time in America, 202 miles over unfamiliar country and without any map, the author's 212-mile goal flight would not have been possible without one. Especially during the latter part of the flight he had to refer to it frequently as a change in wind direction and velocity made it necessary to allow for considerable drifting while flying crosswind.

On a goal flight a pilot stakes his experience and reputation to make his announced destination; it follows naturally that he should have a good deal of distance soaring experience before attempting such a flight. It is a good idea to make it to an airport from which it will be possible to be airplane towed back to the starting point.

The third category of distance soaring is distance to a pre-announced destination with return to the point of departure. This is made without landing at the turning point, where an official observer must be stationed. Notable distance and return flights have been made with the first half into a moderate wind and the return trip back with the wind. Real record possibilities for this type of flight exist along the long, continuous ridges in the Allegheny Mountains where the flight can be made mostly on slope winds reinforced by thermals while flying crosswind each way.

ALTITUDE SOARING

Altitude soaring ranks on a par with distance soaring with respect to its value in pilot training, meteorological research and thrill for the sportsman pilot. However, record attempts involving instrument flying in cumulonimbus clouds with possibilities of extremely turbulent air, lightning, hail, freezing cold and lack of oxygen are far more hazardous than other types of soaring.

It is necessary to have a strong sailplane stressed to diving speeds of 200 m.p.h. with good inherent stability and equipped with brake flaps and a complete set of instruments. These should include, in addition to those necessary for distance soaring, a good turn and bank indicator, preferably an electric type operated by dry cell batteries. The usual type worked by a venturi on the outside of the fuselage is likely to become inoperative when needed most because of moisture and ice clogging the venturi. A clinometer is also helpful. A parachute must be worn on altitude record attempts. Warm clothing is also essential.

The first mark that a student pilot tries for is the 3280 feet above point of release for one of the requirements of his "Silver C" license. This is comparatively simple and requires no more than the usual thermal soaring technique already described. This altitude probably will be exceeded by him on his first cross-country flight which need not and should not involve any cloud flying.

By cloud flying is meant soaring inside clouds by the use of instruments. It is very helpful and also wise for a student to get some dual instrument flying training in an airplane or in a Link Trainer. The latter is a machine widely used for this type of training as it operates indoors and closely approximates actual flight.

Lacking the facilities or funds first to acquire such training, an experienced and capable pilot can teach himself instrument flying quite safely if he is careful. He should first get used to the turn and bank indicator in continuous spirals. At a good altitude of several thousand feet, preferably in quiet, clear air, he should keep the ball centered and the needle of the turn indicator held slightly to one side as he makes continuous, shallow turns. With his eyes on the instruments and not looking outside, he should keep the air speed constant with his control stick. All the time he must remember that in instrument flying his bodily sensations are of little or no value to him after the first few minutes of becoming "blind" or unable to orient himself by visual reference to ground, horizon, or clouds. He must learn to trust his instruments and not his feelings.

The first attempts of cloud flying should be in cumulus clouds of medium size and in which there is little turbulence. After first flying into such a cloud by being lifted up into it from below or flying into the side of it higher up, it is a good idea to fly straight through it or to turn gradually so as to come out soon into clear air. Repeated sorties like this into the cloud will give the pilot confidence to try more without danger of losing control.

On entering a growing cumulus cloud, the pilot will usually notice an increase of lift due to the heat liberated by the process of condensation forming the cloud. He may also find the air within the cloud to be very turbulent, although sometimes the area of best lift within a cloud is quite smooth. If it is smooth the pilot should start a gradual, continuous turn as he watches his turn and bank, airspeed clinometer, and variometer. It is best to limit this first spiral to about 5 minutes and then level out and hold a steady compass course to fly out into clear air. Instrument flying is difficult and quite a strain on the nerves so it is wise to take it in small doses at first and gradually work up until it is possible to stay within a cloud for an hour and longer.

If bad turbulence is encountered at any time the student pilot should straighten up and fly out of the cloud. If he should get completely mixed up and lose control, which is very easy, he should open up his brake flaps, or double spoilers, to prevent excessive speed in a possible dive. Some pilots prefer to put their sailplanes,

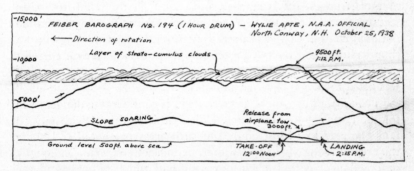

BAROGRAM OF ALTITUDE FLIGHT MADE BY AUTHOR ON OCTOBER 25, 1938

particularly if they are not overly strong, into spins to get out of the cloud without overstraining the wings.

A common fault of pilots attempting altitude flights is that they do not penetrate deeply enough into a cloud before starting to spiral. They may be quite content to rise at 5 to 10 feet per second near the edge of the cloud, not realizing that the lift would be better than 20 feet per second in the center of the cloud. It is best to watch the variometer carefully while flying straight into the cloud heading for its center, and not to start turning until the area of strongest lift is reached. In most variometers there is some lag for which it is necessary to allow for best results. The ability to do this properly can come only from experience.

Before any attempt to set an altitude record or qualify for one requirement for the "Golden C," 10,000 feet above the point of release, by cloud flying, a pilot should have plenty of experience in gaining heights of 500 to 3000 feet inside of cumulus clouds. When he has this background of experience he should pick with care his cloud for the high altitude climb. A large, towering, and rapidly forming cloud is often characterized by slightly curved, flat "cap clouds" which form over the top of the cumulus which soon pushes up through them as they slide down over its "shoulders" as others again form on top and the process is repeated. The most satisfactory method to reach such a cloud is by airplane towing to it and releasing under it. If this type of launching is used it is necessary to carry a sealed barograph in both airplane and sailplane and have the airplane pilot an official observer to get credit for the altitude which counts only above the point of release.

Lift in such a large cloud, which should be utilized before it reaches the dangerous proportions of a nimbus and becomes a thunderstorm, may be as high as 20 to 30 feet per second so that, if the area of strongest lift is reached and stayed in, the climb to 10,000 feet may take only 10 to 15 minutes. During the 1938 German national contest on the Wasserkuppe several pilots went up into a thunderstorm and recorded astoundingly powerful vertical currents of over 60 feet per second. This is 40 m.p.h. straight up! One pilot was lifted to 20,000 feet in 5 minutes.

In conditions as violent as these there is considerable danger even for the most experienced pilot. Unless he is equipped with oxygen tanks he may lose consciousness at such great heights after leaving the area of rising air in which there is sufficient oxygen. An equally serious danger is that of encountering hail which is formed in the terrific up and down currents of a thunderstorm. This may riddle the sailplane with holes, greatly diminishing its lift and control and may also injure the pilot and cause him to lose consciousness. There have been no cases recorded of a sailplane being hit by lightning but theoretically there is no reason why one could not be destroyed by it. Of all these dangers, the one most apt to happen to the pilot is to have his ship thrown out of control, perhaps on its back, and fall into a very fast dive and then be broken up by the sudden and terrific stresses imposed by the violently turbulent air currents. The soaring pilot who goes up into these conditions to set records and learn more about the movements of the air is a hardy pioneer who deserves great credit.

The most important considerations for successful soaring in any of the categories are careful preparation and constant practice. So much remains to be learned about this ocean of air in which we live that, perhaps in this almost more than in any other human activity, experience remains the best teacher.

CHAPTER X

SOARING SITES

By Lewin B. Barringer

SUITABLE LOCATIONS FOR SOARING ACTIVITY can be classi-
fied under the two headings of slope soaring sites and level country
sites. Wherever accessible, the former should be utilized for preliminary soaring due to the fact that soaring in mechanically deflected upwinds is much easier for the student.

Although local conditions may make a very low ridge suitable in
one locality and a high ridge unsuitable in another, general de-
scriptions of a practical site can be drawn up. An ideal slope soaring
site is one where a field large enough for safe launching by winch
towing is located at the top of or within a quarter of a mile of the
base of a ridge at least a mile long with an even slope of about 45°
and 500 feet high, faced into the prevailing wind. Although it is
not essential, there is a real advantage in having the slope covered
with forest in better deflection of winds striking the face at an
angle, the formation of evening thermals, and pilot protection in
the event of a crash.

It is best that the contours at the base and the top of the ridge
are smoothly rounded as this will prevent the turbulent eddies
caused by abrupt angles. An added advantage is gained if the face
of the ridge is curved into a flattened U with the cup opening faced
into the wind. This will cause a greater concentration of upwind,
making soaring possible even in light breezes. It is also worth while
to have a wide valley of level farm lands to the windward side of
the ridge for thermal production in unstable weather. If there is
another parallel ridge equally high or higher, the first is unsuitable
for soaring unless the other is at least a mile distant to preclude
dangerous possibilities of turbulent eddies from the lee side of the
second ridge.

As few sites can be found where the conditions are just as we
would have them it is well to study the soaring sites already established.

SLOPE SOARING SITES

Elmira, New York

It is appropriate to begin with the Warren E. Eaton Soaring Site on Harris Hill, 5 miles northwest of Elmira, New York. This, the most famous site in America, is the scene of the Annual National Soaring Contests and the only site in the United States developed and improved with government funds.

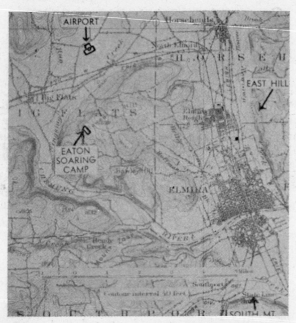

EATON SOARING SITE, ELMIRA

With the better understanding of thermal upcurrents, the Eaton Site has come to replace three other nearby sites: South Mountain, used for north winds; East Hill, for west winds; and a clearing on the ridge overlooking the airport, for south winds. The present size of the take-off field, which is rectangular with the long axis, including a 2500-foot runway, at right angles to the face of the slope, is such that both winch and airplane towing can be done. During the contests there are always a number of visitors who fly in and land on the top.

Present facilities include an administration building, a metal hangar for sailplanes, cabins housing approximately one hundred pilots and crew members, a swimming pool, and parking accommodations for several thousand spectator automobiles. The elevation of the take-off field is close to 1700 feet above sea level and

800 feet above the level valley floor. This valley, known as Big Flats, averages 2½ miles wide opposite the ridge which faces into northwest winds and is of comparatively even contour for soaring with utilities for a length of nearly 2 miles.

In addition to good slope soaring possibilities with northwest winds, this site is excellent for encountering thermals starting in the valley and being accelerated upward by being blown against the ridge. It is on these that the many notable distance as well as altitude flights have been started.

Fred T. Loomis

Warren Eaton Soaring Site on Harris Hill Looking Away from Face of Ridge

L. to R.—Administration building, hangar, part of pilot cabins.

Like the Wasserkuppe in Germany, the Elmira site was started, developed and made famous before the great possibilities of thermal soaring were fully realized. As a starting place for distance records it is far from ideal due to the many miles of dangerous flying country in the wooded Pocono Mountains that must be crossed and the proximity of the Atlantic Ocean when soaring with the prevailing winds. However, perhaps it is best to have such obstacles for competing pilots. The Eaton site is likely to remain the scene for future national contests due to the continued interest and financial assistance of the city of Elmira which rightly calls itself the "Glider Capital of America." It is possible, too, that many of the future altitude records will be made here, but future distance records comparable with the international mark will probably be made over our great plains in the middlewestern states.

Frankfort, Michigan

Quite different from Elmira and ranking second in national prominence are the sites along the sand dunes on the edge of Lake

Michigan near Frankfort, Michigan, scene of the Annual Midwest Soaring Contest and the American Open Soaring Contest. These two contests were combined here August 27 to September 5, 1938, under the managership of the author. Sixty pilots flew 27 gliders for a total of 301 hours, 18 minutes. Best distance was 24.5 miles, best altitude 2000 feet, and best duration 12 hours, 8 minutes. The latter figure, the only outstanding one of the three, indicates that this is primarily a slope soaring site.

The first of the sand dunes in this region discovered as a potential soaring site by Arthur B. Schultz of Detroit and first tested by his partner, John Nowak, is the Sleeping Bear Dune northwest of Empire. This is probably the smoothest soaring ridge known anywhere. Its bare sand face slopes approximately 45° and faces west. It is 500 feet high and 3 miles long and has only one (but serious) defect, which is that west winds have rarely been experienced during soaring meets and expeditions there.

The south end of the ridge bends toward the southeast, presenting a wooded face a mile long for southwest winds which are quite common in the fall. Several flights of 10 hours' duration have been made over it. Launchings and landings have been made on the soft sandy beach to the south of the bend in the ridge. No thermal conditions adequate for cross-country flying have been encountered, although the local thermal effect of warm sands has made flights to 2000 feet altitude possible with sailplanes.

During the second midwest contest in 1937, Schultz and Nowak discovered the Crystal Downs Site, east of Point Betsie and 5 miles north of Frankfort, for use with north winds. The author made the first test flight from auto tow on the beach which is wider and smoother here than that near Empire. Since then this site has been proven to be the best and safest slope soaring site yet found in America. The wide and almost limitless beach making it possible to land anywhere, the ease of winch launching to an altitude even with the top of the ridge, and the smoothness of the airflow make it ideal for training purposes. The remarkable conditions found here were shown by the altitudes of 2000 feet maintained by sailplanes over this 2-mile-long wooded sand ridge which is only from 60 to 200 feet high. The Michigan endurance record of Richard Randolph was made over it, mostly at night.

For west to southwest winds the line of bare sand bluffs bordering the city of Frankfort on Lake Michigan and extending to the south were first utilized during the 1938 contest. Launchings were made by winch tow from the Frankfort beach, the Elberta beach across the inlet, and a field on top of the ridge on the Benson Farm 2 miles

Eliot F. Noyes

THE FIRST TAKE-OFF ON THE CRYSTAL DOWNS BEACH, FRANKFORT, MICHIGAN

Wooded slope and beach to right

LOOKING DOWN ON THE CRYSTAL DOWNS COUNTRY CLUB WHILE SOARING

AIR VIEW OF PT. BETSIE NEAR FRANKFORT, SHOWING SITES FOR THREE WIND DIRECTIONS

In distance, Sleeping Bear Dune, west winds; middle distance, back of Crystal Downs, north winds; foreground, Frankfort Dunes, southwest winds.

south of Frankfort. The slopes vary from 150 to 400 feet high permitting slope soaring for many miles. By judicious jumping of intervening gaps the Albatross high performance sailplane was flown over 24 miles south by Warren Merboth.

In addition to the excellent slope soaring facilities here there are also real possibilities for distance soaring on thermals with north-

ARVIN-SIERRA SOARING SITE

west winds. These thermals can be reached by winch and airplane tow from the Frankfort Airport which also is an ideal training field for primary gliding. It is one of the few places where cumulus clouds form over the bluffs bordering the shore and drift inland. Following the 1938 contest here the Frankfort Soaring Association was formed and this has been followed by a school and a sailplane factory.

Arvin, California

In the southwest the oustanding soaring site and the scene of the principal regional meets is the Arvin-Sierra Soaring Site on the Tejon Ranch near Arvin and Bakersfield in California. Discovered in 1930 by Hawley Bowlus during his soaring activities with Colonel Lindbergh, it was not tried out until the spring of 1937. Located near the south end of the great desert-like San Joaquin

Valley, 10 miles south of Tehachapi Pass, it is on the foothill range of the Sierra Nevada Mountains.

The prevailing westerly wind crosses the valley unobstructed for 30 miles, striking the range almost directly up-slope. Rising from the valley which is here approximately 500 feet above sea level, the foothill slope is steep enough to provide good slope soaring along

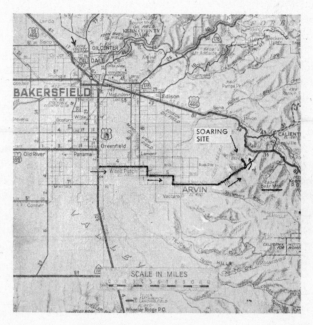

ROUTE TO ARVIN-SIERRA SITE

its brow, which is itself about 1700 feet above the valley floor. Almost directly behind, and within a distance of 2 miles, Bear Mountain rises to a height of 7000 feet. From Bear Mountain, this vast range rises to a maximum of 14,000 feet which extends north and south for a total length of over 400 miles.

The take-off point is a large, nearly level area on top of one of the highest sections of the foothill range. It is unobstructed except for a few trees and rock outcroppings, and there is ample room to permit winch and auto towing and landing on top. One of the best features, from the practicability standpoint, is the accessibility of the site, as a good paved highway leads almost directly up the front of the slope to within a mile of the take-off point. As the highway is also built along the more gentle and smooth sections of the slope, it is generally possible to land near the highway in the event of a "slide" to the valley. Such landings may be observed easily from the take-off point and crews dispatched with very little loss of time. However, in distance flights, pilots may easily find themselves over quite barren and sparsely populated territory. Ranches are scarce all over the valley, and there is little danger, so far as personal safety is concerned. It would be quite possible, however, to land in a spot rather difficult to reach with a car and trailer, to bring back the ship.

Meteorologically, there was much debate and little proof of the merits of the site until the Third Annual Spring Meet in April 1939 when Dick Essery and Paul Hepburn established an American goal flight record for two-seater sailplanes by soaring 43 miles to Taft. This same goal was reached by John Robinson and Woodbridge Brown in single-seaters during the meet.

Most of the operations have been carried on in late summer and fall and at this time of year the temperature is quite high during the day, usually from 90° to 110°. The vegetation is burnt completely, making very little difference in the earth's surface coloring. Also, the humidity is extremely low and there are no bodies of water in the vicinity. Cloud formations, therefore, are not generally prevalent over the valley itself during the late summer months, although clouds do form quite high over the mountain ranges. These are generally at a height of about 8000 to 10,000 feet and so far it has been impossible to reach them.

Torrey Pines Mesa, California

The principal soaring site in the vicinity of San Diego is the Torrey Pines Mesa field developed by the Associated Glider Clubs of Southern California. Located on top of a 300-foot cliff overlooking the Pacific Ocean, it is 18 miles north of San Diego. It is also 3 miles north of La Jolla and 1/4-mile west of U. S. Highway No. 101.

The field, which has runways sufficiently long to permit safe airplane take-offs and landings, is located on a plateau at the edge of a vertical cliff facing due west, varying from 300 to 50 feet in height along the edge of the Pacific for a distance of 5 miles. Over it many hundreds of hours of soaring have been flown in the winds from southwest to northwest.

During spring and summer the prevailing sea breeze from the west, although not very strong, is sufficient to make soaring possible most of the time. Besides the regular airport with its long runways, there are many other fields near the cliff edge that can be used for landings. Also there is a very good beach usable even during high tides nearly the full length of the cliff that can be used for landing

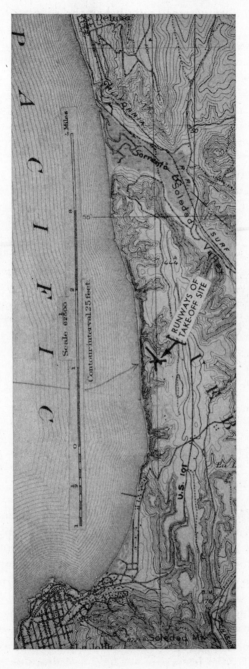

TORREY PINES MESA

if one is so unfortunate as to fly below the edge when the wind dies down.

The glider airport is leased from the City of San Diego by the Associated Glider Clubs of Southern California which is continually improving it. The pilots who have flown most over this site feel that distance soaring from it would be very difficult if not impossible. The longest flight made over it was 9 hours by Woodbridge Brown in his "Swift" sailplane.

Altamount Pass, California

Another well-known California soaring site is that developed on Altamount Pass by the Soaring Society of Northern California. It is located 2 miles south-southwest of Altamount and 1½ miles east-

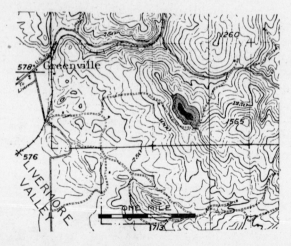

ALTAMOUNT PASS

southeast of Greenville station on the Niles and Sacramento Line of the Southern Pacific Railroad.

A dirt road through the fields leads directly to the top and can be negotiated easily by a car and trailer except during the brief rainy season in the winter. A drive of an hour and a half along U. S. Route 50 brings one to the site from San Francisco, which is about 50 miles to the west.

The take-off site is on the rounded top of a hill approximately half a mile long by 350 yards wide, with the side of the ridge facing southwest. It is 1350 feet above sea level and drops off 700 feet to the westward in gentle slopes to the floor of the Livermore Valley, which runs about 15 miles east and west and averages 5 miles wide.

The slope soaring terrain includes a range of hills continuing nearly 3 miles to the southeast and from 700 to 1000 feet above the valley. For only about a mile is there a clearly defined ridge, the rest being rather cut up by ravines.

The prevailing wind direction is from the west. During the summer months, when there is practically no rain, the winds usually can be relied on to blow about 15 m.p.h. after 2 P.M., which, coupled with the thermal lift, boosts the sailplane from 500 to 1000 feet above the hill.

No distance flights have yet been made from the site, but it seems entirely possible to soar north to Mt. Diablo, which is on a continuation of the same range of hills and 3800 feet high. And from this mountain, a cross-country flight can be made in any direction.

To the south of the site, the Livermore mountains rise to about 3000 feet above sea level. It is also possible to soar along the front of this range to San Jose, a distance of 60 miles. To the east are the San Joaquin and Sacramento Valleys which run about 400 miles north and south. Under favorable conditions it should be possible with a high performance sailplane to make a flight of 200 miles southward to the Tejon Ranch Site in the San Joaquin Valley.

The first trial flight in 1934 lasted 9 minutes. No real effort to set a duration record has been made but the longest flight was 2 hours, 30 minutes, made by J. F. Gough in the "Pegasus" sailplane.

One of the best features of the site is, unfortunately, also one of its greatest drawbacks. The slope most of the way up the hill is gradual enough to permit landings anywhere along it, which is one reason why the site is so practical and safe for sailplane operations. However, these same gentle contours make it practical to plant crops, so the owner of the site has had to restrict its use to the season when crops have been harvested. This prevents soaring here in the spring, when winds are highest and thermals probably strongest.

Schley Field, New Jersey

Located on top of a low ridge about 5 miles south of Bernardsville and 2 miles southwest of Liberty Corners in north central New Jersey, the Schley Glider Field occupies a position unique among American soaring sites. For one thing, it is part of a private estate. For another, it was literally carved out of the forest by the devoted labors of the members of the Aero Club Albatross and the Y Flying Club under the determined and inspiring leadership of Gustave Scheurer, a director of the Soaring Society of America.

As its name implies, it first served as a base of purely gliding activities until the annual meet of the Associated Glider Clubs of New Jersey in 1938, which definitely established it as a soaring site.

The curving ridge on which the field lies extends roughly 30 miles from Paterson to Somerville. The heavily wooded slope down from the field is 300 feet above the level valley. From the point of soaring in purely mechanically deflected slope winds, it is not a very good site, but for the much more important thermal soaring it seems to be excellent, as the ridge is sufficient to give the valley thermals the initial boost to rise to real altitudes.

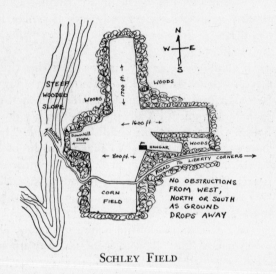

SCHLEY FIELD

Best performances made here to date include a 25-mile goal flight by Floyd Sweet in his Rhönbuzzard sailplane in which he also reached an altitude of 5500 feet, and 3 hours, 23 minutes' duration by Stanley Hruslinski in a Kestrel sailplane.

Wurtsboro, New York

In this same part of the country is the airport near Wurtsboro, New York, for several years the base of operations of the Airhoppers Gliding and Soaring Club. Developed some years previously as an airplane landing field, it was first used for gliders after it became impossible to use the Ellenville Site pioneered by the author with his 155-mile ridge flight on April 2, 1935. This site was on Mt. Mongola but later another was used, 200 feet lower on a shelf of the range named Mt. Meenagha.

The decision of new property owners to stop the soaring activity

came perhaps as a blessing in disguise as this site was large enough
only for hand shock-cord launchings and despite its height of 1200
feet above the valley floor presented difficulties for beginners due
to its uneven contours. At Wurtsboro it is possible to make auto
and winch tows into northwest winds to heights of 400-700 feet,
glide downwind to the ridge of Shawangunk Mountain and soar
up over it. The slope here is quite even, steep, wooded, and rises
870 feet above the field. The practicability of this procedure, which
is easier and safer than shock-cord launchings from the top, was
first proven by Emil Lehecka with his Cadet utility in 1937.

WURTSBORO SITE

The Wurtsboro field is situated on the main highway running
from Kingston, New York, through Ellenville and Port Jervis, 2
miles northeast of the town of Wurtsboro and 80 miles from New
York City. It is 560 feet above sea level, covered with sod and
irregular in shape. The longest runway northeast-southwest is 3400
feet and can be extended to over a mile. The field is the property
of Mr. Lee Helm who has been extremely kind and helpful to the
soaring pilots who have used it.

This site offers great possibilities for student training in gliding
up through high performance soaring. From it can be made flights
meeting all the requirements for the "Silver C" license.

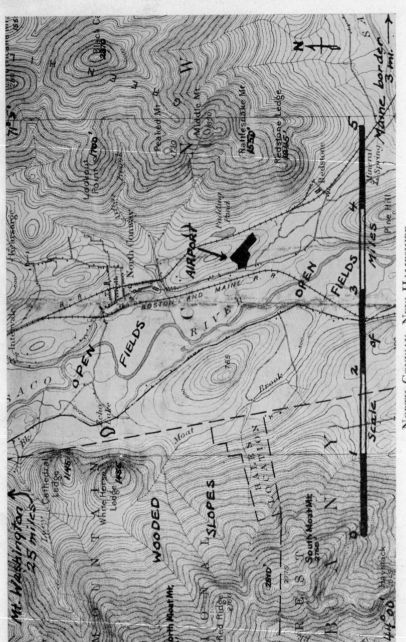

NORTH CONWAY, NEW HAMPSHIRE

North Conway, New Hampshire

What has proven to be the most promising soaring site yet found in New England is the White Mountain Airport. This was pioneered by the author flying the Ross "Ibis" from airplane tow launchings in October 1939. A commercial airport, it is of irregular shape, and located on the main highway between Conway and North Conway, a mile south of the latter town.

The general shape of this field, as well as its proximity to the soaring ridge, can readily be seen on the accompanying map. The surface is grass covered, quite level, and the longest runway is just 2500 feet. The hangar is located in the northwest corner on the main highway, along which a telephone line and pine trees are the obstructions. Trees border the field on all other sides, although approaches with nothing over 15 feet high have been cut leading from the main runways.

Eliot F. Noyes

THE "IBIS" ON WHITE MOUNTAIN AIRPORT LOOKING NORTH ALONG GREEN HILLS RANGE

Elevation of the field is 500 feet above sea level and the highest point of the ridge directly east is 1350 feet above this. Average height is about 900 feet. The nearest point of this wooded ridge steep enough to permit slope soaring is a half mile from the nearest edge of the field.

During a week's stay in the cold weather of the late fall, the author was able to soar on four days. Remarkably strong thermal upcurrents were encountered, making possible new state records of 6500 feet and 2 hours, 23 minutes. The former mark was to an altitude of 9500 feet after releasing from the airplane at 3000. On this flight the sailplane was at times rising at better than 20 feet per second.

There is no doubt that "B" pilots will be able to get their "C" ratings and go right on to the "Silver C" with conditions to be found here on many days throughout the summer months. Duration and altitude far beyond the requirements should be easy. Goal flights can be made to Portland, 50 miles away with northwest winds, and to Boston, 120 miles south, with north winds. Much longer flights can, of course, be made to the south and southwest.

Steptoe Butte, Washington

An old landmark with an interesting historical significance in the "Inland Empire" is Steptoe Butte. It is located on a paved highway

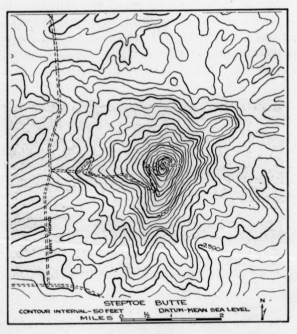

STEPTOE BUTTE

50 miles south of Spokane, Washington. From the highway, the butte is reached by a 5-mile drive on a good dirt road, which zigzags up the face to the top. It is necessary only to go part way up to reach the take-off area.

Steptoe Butte is interesting to enthusiasts of motorless flying for several reasons. It is readily accessible, except in very bad weather. It is a 1100-foot conical peak, facilitating take-off in any direction; and is surrounded by thousands of acres of wheat land, providing excellent landing fields. It has a peculiar formation of two ridges, one extending approximately west and the other nearly south, which give a funnel action to the air, resulting in a strong slope current with a relatively small cross-country wind. This is particularly advantageous in that the prevailing wind is from the southwest. The roads and surrounding country provide good conditions for auto or winch tow, although Steptoe itself is best adapted to shock-cord launching at present.

This site was pioneered by the Washington State College Aero Club and the late Cloyd Artman, who made the first soaring flight in a Mead primary over the butte in the spring of 1935. Since then it has been used every year by the members of the club and several successful meets have been held there. Most outstanding of these was the Annual Spring Meet, April 5 to 12, 1936. A number of flights of from 1 to 5 hours' duration were made during the week. The total time of the 83 flights made was 41 hours, a real proof of the soaring possibilities of this site which will probably continue to play an important role in soaring in the Northwest.

BASE OF THE SOARING SOCIETY OF AMERICA'S LEVEL COUNTRY
EXPEDITION IN 1938
(Taken by the author through Plexiglas windshield while soaring.)

LEVEL COUNTRY SITES

In describing level country sites there is no need for such contour maps as for the slope soaring sites already described. What is required is an airport or other level field sufficiently smooth and large for automobile and winch towing. As a general rule it is best to pick such a site several miles back from the ocean or a large lake due to the temperature inversion so commonly found in such regions. This usually prevents the formation of thermal upcurrents on which the level country pilot must depend.

There are several flat country sites from which successful soaring flights were made in 1938. The first of these, chosen as a base for the author's expedition to the great plains to test this type of soaring, was the Municipal Airport of Wichita Falls, Texas, now site of the Annual Southwestern Soaring Contest. This was a rectangular, grass covered field with longest diagonal measurement of 4000 feet, permitting winch tows in excess of 1000 feet altitude. Statistics of the 27-day expedition in April 1938 show that soaring was done on 15 out of 19 days when the weather was suitable for airplane flying. Thermals were encountered and flights of over 10 minutes' duration were made on 45 of the 81 take-offs by winch tow, an average of 55 per cent. Total flying time was 28 hours, 9 minutes. Best distance, a national record, was 212 miles; best duration, 5 hours, 45 minutes; best altitude, 5524 feet. Later in the summer, Harland Ross, designer of the "Ibis" sailplane, flying a converted Prüfling secondary, reached an altitude of over 7000 feet from auto tow to only 400 feet from a nearby farmer's field.

Simultaneously with or shortly after the experimental flights in Texas, notable flights were made from level country sites in California, Michigan, Ohio, New York and Pennsylvania. John Robinson, flying his self-built intermediate sailplane, "Robin," reached a height of 10,200 feet from an auto tow start to 400 feet on Clark Dry Lake in Borego Valley, 50 miles northeast of San Diego. An interesting technique of catching thermals was used whereby in windless conditions the tow car described wide circles with the glider in tow at the end of the rope until a thermal was encountered.

Elmer Zook, leading pilot of the XYZ Soaring Club of Michigan, made a 36-mile cross-country flight in a standard Franklin utility glider from the Triangle Gliderport near Detroit. This was a little-used airport leased by the Detroit Glider Council and is used now only for gliders, with the exception of a tow plane belonging to one of the glider pilots. Despite the limited area of this field situated in level country, many successful soaring flights have been made from it. Pilots here have used smudge fires to detect thermals.

Richard Randolph, flying a Westpreussen sailplane from the Akron, Ohio, Municipal Airport, reached an altitude of over 7000 feet on thermal upcurrents. Emil Lehecka, flying his Rhönsperber high performance sailplane, made several fine flights from winch tow at Hicksville, Long Island. On one he reached an altitude of over 5000 feet and stayed aloft 2½ hours. Flying the Stevens-Franklin utility glider of his Wings Soaring Club at Pitcairn Field near Philadelphia, the author caught a thermal after releasing from winch tow at a height of 700 feet and rode it to the cloud base at 4700 feet.

Although level country soaring is still very much in its infancy, the success of these flights at such widely scattered locations in varying climatic conditions indicates the great possibilities to be found in this type of soaring which is rapidly making the sport possible in all sections of the country.

Undoubtedly there remain to be discovered and tested many soaring sites in various parts of the country which far exceed the best sites in use today. One ridge site with great possibilities for a school is a spur of an Allegheny mountain ridge 2 miles south of Monteagle, Tennessee. Even contoured and heavily wooded slopes 1000 feet high can be soared over in winds from southwest clockwise around to northeast from one take-off site after it is cleared. Below lies a level farming valley causing powerful thermal upcurrents. This site was discovered by the author on a 4-hour test flight on a cold, cloudless day early in the spring on which a maximum altitude of 6500 feet was easily made. Other potential sites are known in the states of Arizona and Washington. These and many others yet to be discovered can best be tested by an experienced pilot releasing over them from airplane tow.

CHAPTER XI

CLUBS

By Lewin B. Barringer

Aｌｔｈｏｕｇｈ ｔｈｅ ｃｏｓｔ of the average glider is about half the price of the cheapest airplane, it is still beyond the reach of the average youth. The great majority of gliders in the United States are owned by clubs formed by groups of young men sharing the cost. So far only a handful of women have taken up the sport but there is every reason to believe that their participation will grow.

In the formation of a new glider club there are several vital considerations. In order of importance they are as follows: operating base, type and cost of equipment to be built or purchased, storage facilities, number of members, initiation fees and dues, bylaws and insurance.

The organization work is usually done by one live-wire enthusiast, with or without a few helpers. The first step to arouse interest is to hold an organization meeting to which should be asked at least twice as many prospects as the first tentative membership figure. They should all be above fourteen years of age, the minimum. It is wise also to invite one or more older business men, and an experienced glider pilot, if one can be found. To stimulate interest and enthusiasm at the meeting, the club organizers can do no better than to show a moving picture film on motorless flight, such as *Soaring* or *Plane Sailing,* made available to responsible groups by the Soaring Society of America.

Two first-year budgets for typical gliding and soaring clubs of fifteen members each and owning utility gliders are given. The first has new, first-class equipment:

Bｕｄｇｅｔ Cｌｕｂ A

Expenses

New utility glider, trailer	$ 650.00
Instruments (airspeed, altimeter, variometer, ball bank, barograph)	150.00
Used Ford V-8 towcar	100.00
Winch—powered by towcar	150.00
Tow rope	50.00

Car and trailer licenses	20.00
Storage at airport ($10.00 a month)	120.00
Insurance	90.00
Gas and oil	50.00
Repairs and depreciation	70.00
Miscellaneous and reserve	50.00
	$1,500.00

Income

15 Initiation fees	@	$70.00	1,050.00
15 Annual dues	@	$30.00	450.00
			$1,500.00

BUDGET CLUB B

Expenses

Used utility glider, trailer	$ 350.00
Used instruments (airspeed, altimeter, ball bank)	30.00
Used Model A Ford tow car	50.00
Tow rope	30.00
Gas and oil	50.00
Repairs and depreciation	50.00
Miscellaneous and reserve	40.00
	$ 600.00

Income

15 Initiation fees	@	$30.00	$ 450.00
15 Annual dues	@	$10.00	150.00
			$ 600.00

In Budget B it is assumed that operations are on a farmer's field and that the glider is stored in a barn without cost. Car and trailer are not operated elsewhere so are unlicensed. No insurance is carried. In both budgets it is also assumed that instructions are given without charge by a member of the club. Both include sufficient equipment to do slope and thermal soaring after members have completed their preliminary training. The figure for insurance in Budget A includes public liability with limits of $10,000-$20,000, $5000 property damage, and fire and windstorm for the glider based on its value. If it is to be transported cross country on its trailer behind a member's car, a rider should be obtained on the liability insurance policy covering that car; otherwise any possible damage done by the trailer while being towed will not be covered by the liability insurance covering the car.

The best advice for someone anxious to take up gliding if he lives near enough to an established club is to join that club to receive his instruction. Following is a list of active clubs in the United States, compiled by the Soaring Society of America:

American Gliding Clubs

Alabama

Sheffield	Wilson Dam Gliding Club, 712 Raleigh Avenue
University	University of Alabama Glider Club

California

Alameda	Glider Club, 1603 Paru Street
Eureka	Humboldt Flying Club, 523 T Street
Glendale	Aero Soaring Group, 606 W. Vine Street
Los Angeles	Southern California Soaring Ass'n, 738 S. Bristol
Modesto	Modesto Glider Club, 138 Waterford Road
North Hollywood	Mutual Soaring Society, 1126 Huston Street
Pasadena	California Institute of Technology Aero Club
San Diego	Associated Glider Clubs of Southern California, 4141 El Cajon Avenue
San Diego	California Soaring Club, 2820 El Cajon Avenue
San Francisco	Soaring Society of Northern California, 406 Sutter Street
San Mateo	San Carlos Gliding Club, Route 2, Box 3040, Redwood City
Van Nuys	Studio Glider Club, 16005 Basset Street

Colorado

Denver	Broadmoor Sport and Training Camp, 1754 Broadway
Denver	Cactus Glider Club, 1543 Kearney Street

Connecticut

East Hartford	Clark Glider School, Box 76
Waterbury	Waterbury Glider Club, 172 Hamilton Avenue

Delaware

Newark	Delaware College Soaring Club, Evans Hall, University of Delaware
Wilmington	Delaware Soaring Society, 1808 Sycamore Street

Florida

Daytona Beach	Model Airplane and Glider Club, Route 1, Box 218
Gainesville	Seagull Glider Club, University of Florida

Georgia

Atlanta	Atlanta Aero Engineers, 2049 Robson Place, N.E.

IDAHO

Moscow   University of Idaho Glider Club, c/o Ira Jacobsen

Wesleyan   The Gooding College Glider Club

ILLINOIS

Berwyn   Berwyn Glider Club, 2336 So. Lombard Avenue

Chicago   Chicagoland Glider Council, Inc., 1641 Addison Street

Chicago   Gage Park Glider Club, 6919 Yale Avenue

Chicago   Soaring and Gliding Club of Chicago, 4845 Waveland Avenue

Glen Ellyn   Glen Ellyn Glider Club, 482 Main Street

Waukegan   Waukegan Gliding and Soaring Club, 116 S. Martin Avenue

West Chicago   Silver Hawk Glider Club, Air Activities Airport

Zion   Pietschman Gliding School, 3116 Ezra Avenue

INDIANA

Angola   Tri-State Glider Club, 319 S. Darling Street

Attica   Attica Glider Club, West Mill Street

Bremen   Bremen Glider Club

Fort Wayne   Aero Club of Indiana Technical College

Notre Dame   Notre Dame Aeronautical Society, c/o Robert Eikenberry

South Bend   South Bend Glider Club, 1155 N. Meade Street

West Lafayette   Purdue Glider Club, Purdue University Airport

IOWA

Iowa City   Aeronautical Club of the University of Iowa, Engineering Building

KANSAS

Iola   The Iola Gliding Club, 601 Sycamore Street

Manhattan   Kansas State Glider Club, Kansas State College

Topeka   Topeka Soaring Club, 209 Kansas Avenue

Wichita   University of Wichita Glider Club

LOUISIANA

Baton Rouge   Louisiana State University Glider Club, Box 809

New Orleans   Tulane Glider Club, 1831 Bordeaux Street

MARYLAND

Greenbelt   Greenbelt Glider Club, Box 163

Riverdale   Glider Club of Engineering and Research Corporation, c/o H. E. Morehouse

MASSACHUSETTS

Cambridge   Aeronautical Engineering Society, Massachusetts Institute of Technology

Cambridge   Harvard Gliding Club, c/o David Stacey, Sec'y, Kirkland House, G-32

Greenfield   Glider Club of Greenfield, 6 Bowker Street

Westwood   Waco Glider Club, Natuck Airport

Worcester   Worcester Polytechnical Institute Glider Club

MICHIGAN

Ann Arbor	University of Michigan Glider Club
Berkley	ABC Glider Club, 3184 Tyler Avenue
Detroit	Blackhawk Glider Club, 163 Midland Avenue
Detroit	Detroit Glider Council, 15100 Woodward Avenue
Detroit	Lawrence Tech Soaring Society, 15100 Woodward Avenue
Detroit	University of Detroit Glider Club, 16621 Prairie
Frankfort	Frankfort Soaring Association
Milan	Four Ace Glider Club, 151 Wabash Street
Niles	Depoy Motor Company Glider Club, 108 Sycamore Street
Plymouth	XYZ Soaring Club, Triangle Glider Port, R.R. 2
Sault Sainte Marie	Soo Glider Club, c/o Lloyd Gabriel
Suttons Bay	Suttons Bay Glider Club
Wyandotte	Wyandotte Gliding Club, 367 Oak Street

MINNESOTA

Austin	Austin Glider Club, 910 Freeborn Street
Minneapolis	University of Minnesota Flying Club, Glider Section

MISSOURI

Robertson	Curtiss Wright Airplane Co. Glider Club
Rolla	Glider Club of the Missouri School of Mines
St. Louis	Missouri Glider Club, 4915 Argyle Street

MONTANA

Bozeman	Montana State College Glider Club, 522 S. 6 Street

NEBRASKA

Lincoln	University of Nebraska Glider Club, M. E. Bldg.
Omaha	Omaha Aero Club, 4971 Miami Street

NEW HAMPSHIRE

Durham	University of New Hampshire Flying Club
North Conway	Atlosaurus Club, White Mountain Airport

NEW JERSEY

Glen Rock	North Jersey Soaring Association, 34 Cambridge Place
Hillsdale	Pascack Valley Gliding Association, 341 Washington Avenue
Irvington	Aero Club Albatross, 75 Norwood Avenue
Morris Plains	Morristown Glider Club, 2 Sherman Avenue
Newark	Associated Glider Clubs of New Jersey, 91 Halsey Street
Newark	Newark Glider Club, P. O. Box 134
Newark	Y Flying Club, 395 Sussex Avenue
North Haledon	Glider Club, c/o Albert Boyd, High Mountain Road
Wycoff	Ace Gliding Club, c/o John Erlenbach, Jr.

NEW YORK
Albany	Capital Aviation Society, 17 Steuben Street
Buffalo	Buffalo Glider Club, 68 Sanford Avenue
Buffalo	Curtis Gliding and Soaring Association, Engineering Dept., Bell Aircraft Co.
Elmira	Elmira Gliding Club, Federation Building
Elmira	Southside Aeronautical Association, Southside High School
Endicott	Tri-Cities Soaring Society, 1009 Broad Street
Glendale, L. I.	Long Island Gliding Club, 7963 Myrtle Avenue
Ithaca	Ithaca Gliding Club, Ithaca Airport
Inwood, L. I.	Rockaway Gliding and Soaring Club, 20 Lawrence Avenue
Kingston	Glider Club, 130 Pearl Street
Maine	Nanticoke Valley Soaring Society, 20 Main Street
Middletown	Middletown Glider Club, 82 East Avenue
Montauk Pt., L. I.	South Shore Glider Club
New York City	Airhoppers Gliding and Soaring Club, c/o A. Dawydoff, 79 7 Avenue
New York City	Gliding Club of the Boys' Club, 211 East 3 Street
New York City	Metropolitan Soaring Association, c/o C. Gale, 515 Madison Avenue
New York City	S. A. T. Glider Club, Manhattan High School of Aviation, 222 E. 64 Street
Peekskill	Hudson Valley Gliding and Soaring Club, East Main Street
Rochester	Rochester Glider Club, 43 Manchester Street
Troy	Rensselaer Glider Club, Ricketts Laboratory, Rensselaer Polytechnic Institute

OHIO
Akron	Akron Advanced Flying Club, 300 E. Exchange Street
Akron	Akron Glider Council, 277 Brown Street
Akron	University of Akron Glider Club
Cincinnati	Albatross Birdmen, 818 Wade Street
Cincinnati	University of Cincinnati Aero Club
Cleveland	Case Aero Club, Case School of Applied Science, University Circle
Cleveland	C. T. S. Glider Club, Cleveland Trade School, Eagle Avenue
Columbus	Ohio State University Glider Club
Dayton	Dayton Glider Club, 202 Virginia Avenue
Ironton	Valley Glider Club, c/o C. M. Hardy, Tri-State Pattern Works
Kent	Kent State University Glider Club, 615 Park Avenue
New Philadelphia	Tuscarawas Co. Glider Club, Municipal Airport
South Euclid	Beaconwood Glider Club, 1720 Beaconwood Avenue
Toledo	Toledo Gliding Club, Municipal Airport
Xenia	Xenia Glider Club, 310 W. 3 Street

OKLAHOMA

Stillwater	Oklahoma A. & M. Glider Club, Oklahoma Agricultural and Mechanical College
Watonga	Cloud Buster Club, c/o Tom Oler

OREGON

Junction City	Junction City Glider Club

PENNSYLVANIA

Aspinwall	Glider Club of Aspinwall High School
Chester	Pennsylvania Military College Glider Club, c/o George Richardson
Intercourse	Intercourse Glider Club
Philadelphia	Phi Kappa Sigma Glider Club, 3539 Locust Street
Philadelphia	Roxborough Aero Club, Kendrick Recreation Center, Roxborough and Ridge Avenues
Philadelphia	Wings Soaring Club, 422 W. Price St., Germantown
Pittsburgh	Carnegie Tech Glider Club, Carnegie Institute of Technology, Schenley Park
Pittsburgh	Falcon Glider Club, 97 S. 18 Street
Pittsburgh	Glider Club, 10 Virginia Avenue
Pittsburgh	Glider Club of the Boys' Club, 4114 Penn Avenue
Pittsburgh	Gliders Guild, 746 Broughton Street
Pittsburgh	Shadyside Academy, Box 7374, Oakland Station
State College	Penn State Aero Club, 135 S. Frazier Street
Sykesville	Sykesville Gliding and Soaring Club, Box 195

TENNESSEE

Chattanooga	Chattanooga Glider Club

TEXAS

Dallas	Dallas Glider Club, 4516 Fairfax Avenue
Denton	Glider Club, 405 Bernard Street
San Antonio	Aero Club of San Antonio Vocational and Technical School
Wichita Falls	Wichita Falls Soaring Club, 911 8 Street

UTAH

Mt. Pleasant	Mt. Pleasant Glider Club
Roosevelt	Roosevelt Glider Club, Box 172
Salt Lake City	Salt Lake City Glider Club, 2376 S. 8 Street, East

VERMONT

Weirton	Weir High Glider Club

VIRGINIA

Charlottesville	University of Virginia Glider Club, Engineering School
Del Ray	VMS-3R Glider Club, 3405 Randolph Avenue
Front Royal	Glider Club, c/o Seddon Nelson, American Viscose Co.

WASHINGTON

Pullman	State College of Washington Aero Club, Box 958, College Station
Seattle	Cooperative Flying Club, 5012 22 Avenue
Seattle	Howlee Hawks, 3215 W. Genesse
Seattle	Seahurst Gliding Society, 149th and 21 Street, N.W.
Seattle	Seattle Glider Council, c/o Amos Wood, 2659 47 Street, S.W.
Seattle	Tahoma Soaring Club, 4827 Henderson Street

WEST VIRGINIA

Wheeling	Wheeling Aero Club, c/o Kenneth Halpny, 7th and Market Streets

WISCONSIN

Neenah	Glider Club, 414 Oak Street

To consolidate the activities of several clubs in a locality there have been formed regional associations. These are located at the large centers of population. In some cases a small club will call itself an association or a society, which is apt to be confusing. Not including any of these, the leading groups, all affiliated with the national organization, The Soaring Society of America, P. O. Box 71, Elmira, New York, are as follows: on the East coast, the Metropolitan Soaring Association, New York City, and the Associated Glider Clubs of New Jersey, Newark, N. J.; in the middle west, the Akron Glider Council, Akron, Ohio, the Detroit Glider Council, Detroit, Michigan, and the Chicagoland Glider Council, Chicago, Illinois; on the West coast, the Seattle Glider Council, Seattle, Washington, The Soaring Society of Northern California, San Francisco, The Southern California Soaring Association, Los Angeles, and the Associated Glider Clubs of Southern California, in San Diego, California.

Clarence Lee Dale

THE FIRST TAKE-OFF AT WICHITA FALLS, TEXAS, APRIL 9, 1938

BRITISH GLIDING CLUBS

*Compiled by the British Gliding Association,
119, Piccadilly, London, W.1*

Beacon Hill Gliding Club, W. P. Harris, Sec., 22 Hamlet Road, Southend, Essex.

Bristol Gliding Club, H. H. Maufe, Hambrook House, Hambrook.

Cambridge University Gliding Club, J. W. S. Pringle, 1 Benet Street, Cambridge. Flying ground at Caxton Gibbett.

Channel Gliding Club, F. G. Whitnall, 16 High Street, Cheriton, Folkestone. Hangar at Arpinge

Cornwall Gliding Club, J. W. Graham, Red House, Tywardreath. Flying ground at Rosenannon Downs.

Cotswold Gliding Club, J. D. Pether, Culver's Close, Burford, Oxon. Training at Minster Lonell.

Croydon Gliding Club, N. V. Marshall, Hollydena, West Hill, Epsom.

Derbyshire and Lancashire Gliding Club, C. Kaye, 63 Clarkhouse Road, Sheffield. Headquarters at Camphill, Great Hucklow.

Devon Gliding Club, S. G. Tolman, Journal Office, Exmouth.

Dorset Gliding Club, L. A. Lansdowne, The Portman Arms Hotel, East Chinnock, Leovil, Somerset. Flying at Maiden Newton and Kimmeridge.

East Grinstead Gliding Club, G. J. Smith, "Tolskity," Sackville Lane, East Grinstead, Sussex.

Essex Gliding Club, W. Webster, 113, Coombes Road, Dagenham.

Furness Gliding Club, J. S. Redshaw, 18, Fairfield Lane, Barrow-in-Furness, Lancashire. Soaring sites at Moorside and Bootle Fell, Cumberland.

Harrogate Gliding Club, E. T. W. Addyman, The White House, Starbeek, Harrogate.

Hull Gliding Club, R. E Havercraft, 216, Park Avenue, Hull. Flying ground at Hendon Aerodrome.

Imperial College Gliding Club, Imperial College of Science, South Kensington, London, S.W. 7. Flying at Dunstable Downs.

Kent Gliding Club, Miss R. H. Sinclair, Lade Place, Sutton Courtenay, Berkshire. Training ground at Lenham.

London Gliding Club, Tring Road, Dunstable, Bedfordshire. Clubhouse, hangar, flying ground at Dunstable.

Midland Gliding Club, M. F. Barnes, 100, Holly Road, Birmingham 20. Soaring site at Long Mynd, 3 mi. WSW of Shurch Stretton, Salop.

Newcastle Gliding Club, A. P. Miller, 25, Home Avenue, Walkerville, Newcastle-on-Tyne, 6. Soaring site at Chillingham.

Norfolk and Norwich Aero Club, Gliding Section, J. F. Taunton, Municipal Aerodrome, Norwich.

Oxford University and City Gliding Club, Mrs. H. Aspell, 5, Holywell, Oxford.

Portsmouth and South Harts Gliding Club, R. G. H. Parnell, 128, New Road, Portsmouth. Flying ground at Portsdown Hill.

Southdown Gliding Club, A. York Bramble, 7 a, First Avenue, Hove 3, Sussex. Flying grounds at Devil's Dyke, Brighton.

Yorkshire Gliding Club, L. A. Alderson, 32, Wensley Green, Chapel Allerton, Leeds 7. Flying ground at Sutton Bank.

SCOTLAND

Dumbartonshire Gliding Club, J. V. Campbell, Kirklea, Cardross Road, Dumbarton.

Inverness Gliding Club, F. Oliver, 13, Leys Drive, Inverness.

Perth Gliding Club, R. Mackelvie, View Cottage, Union Road, Scone, Perthshire.

Scottish Gliding Union, J. W. Gardner, Journal Office, Alloa. Soaring site at Lomond Hills, Fifeshire.

NORTHERN IRELAND

Ulster Gliding Club, N. P. Metcalfe, c/o Ulster Spinning Co., Ltd., Belfast. Flying ground at Downhill, Magilligan Strand, Londonderry.

CHANNEL ISLANDS

Jersey Gliding Club, A. J. Scriven, Quainton, Samares, Jersey. Flying ground at north end, St. Quen's Bay.

WALES

Swansea and District Gliding Club, A. H. Knott, 209 a, High Street, Swansea.

Antelo Devereux

SAILPLANE WING

Successful club operation is usually the result of fine teamwork and whole-hearted helpfulness on the part of all members of the club. Of necessity the sport is one of cooperation where several on the ground work to get one into the air. Through this unselfish cooperation, the members of gliding clubs often demonstrate the finest type of sportsmanship, which is one of the worthwhile attributes of motorless flying.

CHAPTER XII

FUTURE OF GLIDING AND SOARING

By Lewin B. Barringer

THE ONLY WAY TO GET AN IDEA of what will be done in the field of motorless flying in the future is first to procure a clear picture of what it is and does at the present time. Primarily gliding and soaring should be considered as a sport.

Soaring can be compared more nearly with sailing than with any other sport, as one can truly say that it is the sailing of the air. In soaring we also use lateral winds to help us on our way in addition to the vertical winds to keep us aloft. Those who follow the sea in sailing should be among the first to take to the air in soaring as so many of the stimulating elements that make sailing attractive are found in gliding and soaring intensified to a greater degree.

As a sport, gliding has such worthwhile attributes as healthy, outdoor exercise, sportsmanship, cooperation, and the building of keen judgment and self-reliance. Essentially it is a cooperative sport requiring the help of a number of persons to get one into the air. Assembly of gliders, laying out towropes, pulling ships into line for take-off, retrieving them after landing, running with a wing tip, stretching shock cord, and waving signal flags all call for a certain amount of exercise in addition to concentration which will keep members of gliding clubs happily and healthfully engaged in the open air.

Without exaggeration gliding and soaring is one of the cleanest of sports from every point of view. The fine sportsmanship shown by our leading soaring pilots during keen competition at national contests has been of the highest order. This same unselfish spirit can also be found in a week-end outing of a small glider club where members seem to get as much enjoyment in helping to launch one of their number as in doing the flying themselves. It is also manifest in the tremendous amount of work that many boys are willing to do to build and maintain their gliders.

Any glider pilot who builds himself up to the ranks of the expert soaring pilots adds tremendously to his general knowledge, good judgment and self-reliance. To be a successful soaring pilot one must be able to think quickly and clearly, and this sharpening of mental processes is bound to be advantageous in later life.

Quite aside from the worthwhile attributes of motorless flying as a sport are its practical advantages. The principal ones are usually grouped under the three headings of flight training, aircraft design, and meteorological research.

It has been proven that with the use of proper equipment under capable supervision and along accepted lines of procedure as described in this book gliding offers the safest, most thorough and most economical way to learn to fly fixed-wing, heavier-than-air craft. Using a steel tube utility glider with good flying characteristics, a student can learn to fly with a maximum of safety due to its low stalling speed, level landing attitude, and the pilot protection of its fuselage structure.

Eliot F. Noyes

PILOTS AWAITING THEIR TURNS TO TAKE OFF AT A NATIONAL
CONTEST, ELMIRA, N. Y.

Primary gliding flight training is largely self taught, and like most knowledge thus acquired, it is always remembered by the student. Unlike primary instruction with airplanes the student learns to land the glider very soon as he works his way gradually higher with complete confidence. Learning to land with an airplane with its greater gliding speed is more difficult and consequently requires more time. A true sense of flying "feel," as the student glider pilot acquires it without the use of instruments, is invaluable in developing real flying ability.

The fact that a glider is making a "forced landing" every time it comes to earth of necessity develops a fine sense of judgment in the pilot. Unlike the airplane pilot he cannot fall back onto his motor to lift him over the trees, telephone wires or other obstructions at the edge of the landing field after he has undershot. Consequently the experienced glider pilot makes the safest airplane pilot. Confronted with a forced landing due to engine failure he can fall back on the experience gained in making many hundreds and perhaps thousands of landings. He cannot afford to misjudge and consequently takes care not to.

Advanced or "high performance" soaring can be of really great advantage in giving an airplane pilot a thorough knowledge of the movements of the atmosphere. In fact, it is the only way now known for him to acquire from first-hand observation this understanding essential to make him a well-rounded pilot whether he flies commercially or for pleasure. The reason for this is that he is unable to get a true feel of rising or falling air currents when cutting through them at the speed of the average airplane. On the other

Maxwell Fredric Coplan

SOARING MAKES BETTER AIRPLANE PILOTS
The author flies over the mountainous terrain of Iran.

hand, a light sailplane, flying at 35 to 50 m.p.h., rides the currents in such a fashion that the pilot soon finds out just what is going on, particularly with the aid of the sensitive instruments developed for soaring flight. A suitable comparison is a light sailboat riding the waves compared with a speedboat cutting through them.

That many experienced airmen do not fully appreciate the danger of violent up- and down-currents has been shown by the wreckage of several large airplanes which have been torn apart in flight through thunderstorms. The larger that airplanes are built and the faster they are flown the more serious this problem will become. One does not have to be an engineer to appreciate the enormous stresses that can be set up in the structure of a 150-foot span airplane flying at 250 m.p.h. through storm conditions where one wing may suddenly go through a current rising vertically at a speed of 100 m.p.h and the other wing at the same time in an equally strong downcurrent. It is the author's firm belief that we will never be able to build aircraft sufficiently strong to fly safely through all the atmospheric disturbances that may be encountered. The answer is obvious: we must learn thoroughly to understand the dangerous conditions and avoid them.

In Germany, the nation that has so far led the world in motorless flying, the great Lufthansa airways system owns a number of high performance sailplanes for its pilots to fly in their off hours. After being checked out in two-seaters, they are allowed to soar in single-seaters. The most experienced instrument flying pilot of this

Herald-Times Photo

NOTED AIRCRAFT ENGINEERS WITNESS SAILPLANE DEMONSTRATION AT BOLLING FIELD

L. to R.—Dr. Eastman Jacobs; Dr. George Lewis, Director of the NACA; the author; Mr. Fred Weick.

line, Dreschel, set the world soaring altitude record in 1938. It is also undoubtedly the fact that the successful long distance flights of the Graf Zeppelin and other German dirigibles can be attributed in no small degree to German thoroughness in using meteorological knowledge, largely augmented by soaring, to avoid disturbances in which these craft are particularly vulnerable.

To sum up, wherever possible a student pilot should be trained first in a utility glider, then in a two-seater sailplane or a lightplane, followed by soaring in high performance sailplanes before as well as during the period of flying more powerful and faster airplanes. Nothing is so good for the pilot of large, heavy airplanes, who has been lulled into a sense of security akin to boredom by thousands of hours of routine flight, as to go out at regular intervals and fly a sailplane which will keep him on his toes while having the time of his life. Most of the airplane pilots, who, like the author, were introduced to soaring, agree with him that when they want to enjoy flying to the utmost they go aloft without an engine.

In the field of aeronautical engineering, gliding and soaring development has played a not inconsiderable role. Sailplane designers intent only on improving the design of soaring craft for maximum efficiency have arrived at structural designs that have proven of real value in airplane designing. Some of the features developed in motorless aircraft and later incorporated in airplanes are highly tapered wings, monospar wing construction, wing-fuselage connections, fuselage and cockpit design. Igor Sikorski, the famous flying boat designer, stated that the wing of one of his great four-motored "Clipper" ships followed closely the design of a sailplane wing he had seen while attending a national soaring contest at Elmira.

In Germany such devices as flaps, slots, etc., designed for use on large airplanes, frequently are installed first on a small scale on sailplanes for testing. With the tremendous diving speeds possible on aerobatic sailplanes like the "Habicht," which is stressed for 280 m.p.h., it is possible to approximate closely actual airplane flight conditions at comparatively low cost.

Last, but certainly not least in importance of the three principal categories of the practical application of motorless flight, is that of meteorological research. It has been proved that an experienced pilot flying a high performance sailplane equipped with the proper recording instruments can obtain a better cross-section picture of atmospheric phenomena than can be obtained by any other means. A sailplane flies slowly enough for its pilot to feel and experience atmospheric movements.

It has been the author's practice on cross-country or altitude soaring flights to carry a thermometer and hygrometer installed to give true readings of the outside air and to make notes of these readings at various times and altitudes. Of greater value would be automatic recording instruments such as a thermobarograph which keeps a graph of temperature as well as altitude. These notes augmented by a running log of velocity of up- and downcurrents were copied after landing, on a mimeographed form made up with the assistance of the Meteorological Committee of the Air Transport

FLIGHT LOG

Date _October 25, 1939_   Location _North Conway, N.H._
Sailplane _Ross "Ibis"_   License No. _NX17623_
Pilot _Lewin B. Barringer_   License No. _30984_
Take Off: Time _12:00 Noon_   Landing: Place _White Mt. Airport_

Type of Launching _Airplane tow (Waco C)_   Time _2:15 P.M._

Altitude of Release _3,000 ft._

Meteorological Observations:

	Wind Dir. & Vel.	Pressure	Temperature	% Humidity	Altitude
Take Off	WNW 15	29.8	65°F	40	500 ft.
Highest Altitude (Estimate)	NW 35		12°F	95	9,500 ft.
Landing	Calm	29.8	70°F		500 ft.

General Observations: (Route, strongest lift, relationship of thermals to details of terrain and topography, cloud types, relationship of features observed to general situation (fronts, instability)

Encountered strong thermal at 300 ft. (too low over trees to release) Cut loose over Hurricane Mt. Immediate strong lift of 4-10 ft./sec. Strong thermals all over Green Hills ridge, especially over ravines of Artist Brook 12:30 P.M. - alt. 5,300 ft. - Temperature 29°F - Humidity 78% Base of strato-cumulus overcast. Lift so strong could not help going into clouds. 12:45 - still in clouds at 7,200 ft. Temp. 18°, Humidity 100. Occasionally trying to lose alt. in openings between clouds found here strongest lift of at least 20 ft./sec. Climbed 1,500 above overcast to max. alt. of 9,500 ft. Warm in cockpit although only 12° outside. Sank rapidly through 2,000 cloud layer. Rest of flight slope soaring below 3,000 ft. until wind changed to North and died down. Tested ridge from Redstone Ledge to Cranmore Ski Slope. Found no bad turbulence anywhere. This is an excellent site for preliminary soaring. — L.B.B.

Airline Distance Covered _None (Return to point of departure)_
Witnesses Signatures and Addresses. _Actually flew 10 miles across Main border to East._
Take Off 1. _Theodore Bellak, Newark, N.J._
2. _Wylie Apte, North Conway, N.H._
Landing 1. _Theodore Bellak, Newark, N.J._
2. _Wylie Apte, North Conway, N.H._

METEOROLOGICAL FORM DESIGNED AND USED BY AUTHOR FOR
SOARING RESEARCH

Association, composed of the chief meteorologists of the principal airlines in the United States. As the number of these forms sent in with detailed weather maps of general conditions at the time of the flights increases, they will form a valuable reference file for the study of meteorology.

Having reviewed the different aspects of present-day motorless flight activities it is safe to make the prophecy that it will continue to grow until many thousands of devotees will be soaring in many countries. Due to the fact that it is the cheapest way to fly, it offers the only means for the average man to get into the air.

Many of the present practical drawbacks can be eliminated by the development of a power soarer. This term of "power soarer" conveys rather a different meaning than "power glider." It refers to a sailplane equipped with an auxiliary engine to facilitate take-offs and transportation to and from soaring sites. If applied in this manner, a small engine will no more make an airplane out of a high performance sailplane than an auxiliary engine makes a speedboat out of a sailing yacht. After all, we use an engine in an auto, winch or airplane tow launching, so why not incorporate a small engine into the sailplane itself, to make it possible to take off and climb to an altitude where thermals can be caught? By doing this we will eliminate a great deal of the trouble of a ground crew as well as the possible danger to other aircraft of using long tow ropes on an airport.

It is quite possible to design a sailplane with the motor down inside the fuselage, completely out of the slipstream, and cooled by louvres which can be closed by flaps when soaring, on the sides and bottom of the fuselage. Power could be applied through gearing to a small propeller mounted on a streamlined mast. The propeller could be made "free wheeling" with power off, or could be locked and retracted with the mast into the fuselage.

At a soaring contest it would be an easy matter for the official in charge to limit the gasoline supply to an amount sufficient to reach a certain altitude, such as 1500 meters, the maximum allowed by the F.A.I. for airplane tows in contest soaring. The engine vibration recorded on the barograph would probably show the exact altitude as well as the time that the pilot shut off his engine and started to use thermal updrafts to carry him aloft, as well as speed him on his way.

Let us look into the not-too-distant future and imagine the ease and convenience of rolling your sailplane out of the hangar by yourself, as it is balanced on its two-wheel landing gear, with wheels set on either side of the skid. Out on the concrete apron you unfold the wings, lock them in position, head the ship into the wind, climb into the cockpit, shut down the hood, and strap yourself in. After a few shots of the primer, you press the self-starter button and the little engine comes to life. Holding the stick back and the brakes on, you let it warm up for a few minutes.

Taxiing out to the end of a runway, you keep out of the way of a landing transport and wait for the green light of the control tower before pushing the throttle forward. Taking off gracefully, you retract the wheels and fly away from the airport toward some likely looking cumulus clouds. At 1500 feet your variometer suddenly jumps from 7 feet per second to 12. Immediately you start to spiral, as you shut off the ignition switch, apply the propeller brake until it stops in the up and down locked position, and then pull the retracting lever. The rate of climb drops back to 5 feet per second, but there is now no noise, no vibration, nothing but the silence, the beauty of soaring flight.

Five hours later and 180 miles from home, you run out of thermals. At 1000 feet you pull up your propeller, start the engine and head for a nearby airport. A few minutes later you circle the field, drop your wheels, pull on the flaps and come in to land. Your sailplane is stored overnight in a hangar and, next day, you fill up your tank and fly home.

APPENDIX

GLIDING AND SOARING LICENSES
LICENSE PINS for MOTORLESS FLIGHT

"A"   "B"   "C"   "Silver C"

GLIDING   SOARING

"A"—Two gliding flights of at least 1 minute duration, "S" turn, normal landing.

"B"—Two gliding flights with 360° turns, one to right and one to left, landing so as to come to a stop within 100 feet of a designated mark.

"C"—One soaring flight in which an altitude greater than that at the starting or releasing point is maintained for at least 5 minutes.

"SILVER C"—Two or three soaring flights in which the three following requirements are made:
(1) Distance, 32 miles (50 km.); (2) Altitude, 3280 feet (1000 m.); (3) Duration, 5 hours.

"GOLDEN C"—(1) Possession of "Silver C" license; (2) Distance, 185 miles (300 km.); (3) Altitude, 10,000 feet (3000 m.).

The "A," "B" and "C" licenses are awarded by the National Aeronautic Association through the Soaring Society of America, Inc., P.O. Box 71, Elmira, New York, and the qualifying flights for them must be witnessed by an official Glider Observer. The "Silver C" and "Golden C" are awarded by the International Student Commission for Motorless Flight (ISTUS) with headquarters in Germany through its American representative, the Soaring Society of America. Qualifying flights must be witnessed by an Official Glider Observer and a sealed barograph must be carried on all qualifying flights with the possible exception of the 5-hour duration provided it is made within sight of the observer.

CIVIL CERTIFICATES

The Civil Aeronautics Authority of the United States Government issues to pilots of motorless aircraft licenses, known as certificates of competency, which are now required by law in many states. The three grades with their requirements are as follows:

STUDENT GLIDER PILOT RATING. To be eligible for a student glider pilot rating, an applicant shall comply with the following minimum requirements:

Age. Applicant shall be at least 14 years of age. If applicant be less than 21 years of age at the time of making application, he shall submit with his application the written consent of either parent, or legal or natural guardian, to the issuance of the glider pilot rating sought.

Character. Applicant shall be of good moral character.

Citizenship. Applicant may be a citizen of any nationality.

Education. Applicant shall be able to read, speak, write and understand the English language; except that a citizen of a country granting reciprocal pilot privileges to pilots of the United States on equal terms and conditions will not be required to meet the English language requirements.

Physical condition. Applicant shall certify that to the best of his knowledge and belief he has no physical defect which renders him incompetent to pilot a glider.

Aeronautical knowledge. No minimum requirements.

Aeronautical experience. No minimum requirements.

Aeronautical skill. No minimum requirement, but prior to his first solo flight a student glider pilot shall, in the opinion of his instructor, be deemed competent to make such solo flight.

PRIVATE GLIDER PILOT RATING. To be eligible for a private glider pilot rating, an applicant shall comply with the following minimum requirements:

Age. Same as for student pilot.

Character. Same as for student pilot.

Citizenship. Same as for student pilot.

Education. Same as for student pilot.

Physical condition. Same as for student pilot.

Aeronautical knowledge. Applicant shall be familiar with and accomplish satisfactorily a written examination on the provisions of Air Traffic Rules.

Aeronautical experience. Applicant shall have completed at least 100 gliding flights, 25 of which shall have each included a 360° turn, and at least 5 of such 25 flights shall have been made within the 30 days preceding the date of filing the application.

Aeronautical skill. Applicant shall demonstrate his ability to pilot a glider by satisfactorily making at least the following: one straight flight with normal take-off and landing within the airport; one flight with a 180° turn and a down-wind landing in wind of not more than 10 m.p.h. velocity; one flight with a 360° turn to the right and a landing to within 200 feet of a designated mark; and one flight with a 360° turn to the left and a similar landing.

COMMERCIAL GLIDER PILOT RATING. To be eligible for a commercial glider pilot rating, an applicant shall comply with the following minimum requirements:

Age. Same as for student pilot except that applicant shall be at least 18 years of age.

Character. Same as foregoing.

Citizenship. Same as foregoing.

Education. Same as foregoing.

Physical condition. Applicant shall comply with the following minimum requirements as to physical condition; provided, that the existence of a lesser grade or condition in one or more of the particulars mentioned may not disqualify the applicant if excellence in other particulars or excellence in aeronautical experience or in aeronautical skill offsets the deficiency in the opinion of the Secretary; provided, that an applicant having structural defects or limitations which, in the opinion of the Secretary, may interfere with the safe piloting by the applicant of other aircraft, may be certificated to pilot only such aircraft as are specified by the Secretary in the pilot certificate of such applicant, provided, however, that an increase of such deficiency, which occurs at any time within the effective period of the certificate and cannot be compensated for by some additional excellence (as in aeronautical experience or practical skill), will automatically invalidate such certificate.

(a) *Eye.* Applicant shall have a visual acuity of at least 20/50 in each eye separately, without correction; provided that, if the vision in either or both eyes is poorer than 20/50 and is brought up to 20/30 or better in each eye by glasses, the applicant may be qualified on condition that correcting glasses be worn while piloting aircraft. An average of 30 millimeters or less on the depth perception apparatus, with or without glasses, is required. If the depth perception is greater than 30 millimeters without correction and can be corrected to at least 30 millimeters by glasses, the restriction that correcting glasses be worn while piloting aircraft will apply. No diplopia will be allowed unless corrected by glasses, in which case such glasses must be worn while piloting aircraft. There shall be no serious pathology of the eye.

(b) *Ear, nose, throat and equilibrium.* Applicant shall be able to hear the whispered voice at 3 feet; shall have no acute or chronic disease of the internal ear, no disease or malformation of the nose or throat which may interfere with or be aggravated by flying, and no disturbance in equilibrium.

(c) *General physical conditions.* Applicant shall have no organic or functional disease or structural defect or limitation which might interfere with the safe piloting of aircraft.

(d) *Nervous system.* Applicant shall have no disease of the mental or nervous system and no abnormality of the personality.

Aeronautical knowledge. Applicant shall be familiar with and accomplish satisfactorily a written examination on so much of the provisions of Parts 00, 01, 02, 03, 20, 60, 91, 94 and 98 of the Civil Air Regulations, as are pertinent to his rating.

Aeronautical experience. Applicant shall have completed at least 250 gliding flights, 100 of which shall each have included a 360° turn, and at least 5 of such 100 flights shall have been made within the 30 days preceding the date of filing the application. Applicant shall also have had at least 1 hour of instruction in recovery from stalls and spins in a Class 1 airplane by a certificated instructor, evidenced by the signed entry of such instructor in the log book of the applicant. Five hours of soaring may be substituted for 50 gliding flights.

Aeronautical skill. Applicant shall demonstrate his ability to pilot a glider by satisfactorily making at least the following: one straight flight with normal take-off and landing within the airport; one flight with a 180° turn and a down-wind landing in wind of not more than 10 m.p.h. velocity; one flight with a 360° turn to the right and a landing to a point not more than 100 feet beyond a designated line; one flight with a 360° turn to the left and a similar landing; and two flights including right and left turns in each flight.

STATISTICS OF AMERICAN NATIONAL SOARING CONTESTS

	1931	*1932*	*1933*	*1934*	*1935*	*1936*	*1937*	*1938*	*1939*
Best Distance	15	66	18	158	120	146	133	225	233
Best Altitude	3130	5370	4334	6224	4980	6516	5890	6804	17,264
Best Duration	7:30	8:18	3:16	6:08	7:11	8:48	6:32	7:26	7:20
No. of Gliders	26	18	22	30	31	23	54	20	36
No. of Pilots	36	45	72	63	96	82	147	59	88
Total Hours Flown	26	194	54	117	160	354	242	418	...
Total Mileage Flown	58	189	82	330	330	1283	2224	5841	6808

(Note: The first National Contest was held in 1930, but the statistics are incomplete.)

RECORDS

DISTANCE (SINGLE PLACE)

International	U.S.A.	Great Britain	France	Germany
1891 Lilienthal (G.), 1300 ft.				1891 Lilienthal, 1300 ft.
Aug. 1902 Wright (U.S.A.), 2021 ft.	Aug. 1902 Wright, 2021 ft.			
Oct. 1912 Gutermuth (G.), 2740 ft.				Oct. 1912 Gutermuth, 2740 ft.
April 9, 1920 Klemperer (G.), 1.1 mi.				April 9, 1920 Klemperer, 1.1 mi.
Aug. 25, 1921 Martens (G.), 2.2 mi.				Aug. 25, 1921 Martens, 2.2 mi.
Aug. 19, 1922 Hentzen (G.), 8.6 mi.				Aug. 19, 1922 Hentzen, 8.6 mi.
Sept. 25, 1923 Botsch (G.), 11 mi.				Sept. 25, 1923 Botsch, 11 mi.
Oct. 14, 1924 Martens (G.), 14 mi.				Oct. 14, 1924 Martens, 14 mi.
Oct. 9, 1925 Nehring (G.), 15 mi.				Oct. 9, 1925 Nehring, 15 mi.
Aug. 12, 1926 Kegel (G.), 35 mi.				Aug. 12, 1926 Kegel, 35 mi.
Dec. 18, 1926 Gattaneo (Italy), 44 mi.				
July 30, 1929 Kronfeld (G.), 93 mi.				July 30, 1930 Kronfeld, 93 mi.
Aug. 24, 1930 Kronfeld (G.), 103 mi.				Aug. 24, 1930 Kronfeld, 103 mi.
July 25, 1931 Groenhoff (G.), 137 mi.	1931 Haller, 25 mi.		Aug. 26, 1923 Thoret, 5.6 mi.	July 25, 1931 Groenhoff, 137 mi.

June 7, 1933
Riedel (G.), 143 mi.

1932
O'Meara, 66 mi.
Sept. 1933
duPont, 122 mi.
June 25, 1934
duPont, 158 mi.

June 25, 1934
duPont (U.S.A.), 158 mi.
July 26, 1934
Hirth (G.), 220 mi.
Sept. 27, 1934
Dittmar (G.), 234 mi.
July 21, 1935
Hofmann (G.), 296 mi.
July 29, 1935
Oeltschner (G.), 313 mi.
May 5, 1937
Rastorgoueff (U.S.S.R.), 335 mi.
May 12, 1937
Rastorgoueff (U.S.S.R.), 374 mi.
May 27, 1937
Rastorgoueff (U.S.S.R.), 405 mi.
July 6, 1939
Klepikova (U.S.S.R), 465 mi.

Apr. 12, 1938
Barringer, 212 mi.
June 6, 1939
Brown, 263 mi.

ALTITUDE (SINGLE PLACE)

Aug. 18, 1922
Martens (G.), 351 ft.
Aug. 24, 1922
Hentzen (G.), 1137 ft.

Sept. 23, 1932
Bouvier, 20 mi.

June 7, 1933
Riedel, 143 mi.

Sept. 17, 1934
Nessler, 33.7 mi.

1934
Wills, 105 mi.

Aug. 21, 1937
Nessler, 122 mi.
Apr. 18, 1938
Nessler, 239 mi.

Apr. 30, 1938
Wills, 209 mi.

July 26, 1934
Hirth, 220 mi.
Sept. 27, 1934
Dittmar, 234 mi.
July 21, 1935
Hofmann, 296 mi.
July 29, 1935
Oeltschner, 313 mi.

Jan. 20, 1923
Bossontrot, 246 ft.

Aug. 18, 1922
Martens, 351 ft.
Aug. 24, 1922
Hentzen, 1137 ft.

ALTITUDE (SINGLE PLACE)—continued

International	U.S.A.	Great Britain	France	Germany
Feb. 7, 1923 Descamps (F.), 1774 ft.	July, 1932 O'Meara, 5370 ft.	June 5, 1938 Wills, 10,080 ft.	Feb. 7, 1923 Descamps, 1774 ft.	Aug. 8, 1928 Dittmar, 2530 ft.
July 26, 1925 Auger (F.). 2240 ft.	June 30, 1934 duPont, 6223 ft.		July 26, 1925 Auger, 2240 ft.	Apr. 25, 1929 Nehring, 3868 ft.
Aug. 8, 1928 Dittmar (G.), 2530 ft.	July 5, 1938 duPont, 6804 ft.		Sept. 17, 1934 Nessler, 3267 ft.	July 20, 1929 Kronfeld, 6482 ft.
Apr. 25, 1929 Nehring (G.), 3868 ft.	July 4, 1939 Stanley, 17,264 ft.		May 25, 1935 Roger, 5161 ft.	July 30, 1929 Kronfeld, 8320 ft.
July 20, 1929 Kronfeld (G.), 6482 ft.			March 21, 1938 Lamort, 5926 ft.	Feb. 17, 1934 Dittmar, 14,137 ft.
July 30, 1929 Kronfeld (G.), 8320 ft.			June 30, 1938 Nessler, 11,532 ft.	May 22, 1937 Steinig, 18,720 ft.
Feb. 17, 1934 Dittmar (G.), 14,137 ft.				Aug. 5, 1938 Dreschel, 21,398 ft.
May 22, 1937 Steinig (G.), 18,720 ft.				Nov. 11, 1938 Ziller, 22,434 ft.
Aug. 5, 1938 Dreschel (G.), 21,398 ft.				
Nov. 11, 1938 Ziller, (G.), 22,434 ft.				

DURATION (SINGLE PLACE)

International	U.S.A.	Germany
Jan. 1903 Wright (U.S.A.), 1.1 min.	Jan. 1903 Wright, 1.1 min.	Aug. 30, 1921 Klemperer, 13 min.
Oct., 1911 Wright (U.S.A.), 9.7 min.	Oct., 1911 Wright, 9.7 min.	
Aug. 30, 1921 Klemperer (G.), 13 min.		

Nov. 13, 1921
Harth, 21 min.
Aug. 18, 1922
Martens, 1:06 min.

Oct. 21, 1922
Maneyrol, 3:31
Jan. 3, 1923
Thoret, 7:03

May 3, 1927
Schultz, 14:07

Aug. 3-4, 1933
Schmidt, 36:35

Nov. 25, 1934
Nessler, 11:30
July 22, 1935
Nessler, 16:05

April 19, 1938
Straatman, 53 mi.
April, 1938
Kraft, 116 mi.

May 15, 1938
Reitsch, 155 mi.
July 7, 1938
Flinsch, 191 mi.

1935
Neilan, 12:47
July 31, 1938
Pick, 13:07
Aug. 18, 1938
Young, 15:47

DISTANCE AND RETURN (SINGLE PLACE)

Dec. 17-18, 1931
Cocke, 21:34

July, 1936
duPont, 32 mi.

July, 1939
Decker, 40 mi.

Nov. 13, 1921
Harth (G.), 21 min.
Aug. 18, 1922
Martens (G.), 1 hr. 6 min.
Oct. 21, 1922
Maneyrol (F.), 3:31
Jan. 3, 1923
Thoret (F.), 7:03
July 26, 1925
Massaux (Belg.), 10:30
May 3, 1927
Schultz (G.), 14:07
Dec. 17-18, 1931
Cocke (U.S.A.), 21:34
Aug. 3-4, 1933
Schmidt (G.), 36:35

April 19, 1938
Straatman (G.), 53 mi.
June 10, 1938
Korotor (U.S.S.R.), 119 mi.
July 7, 1938
Flinsch (G.), 191 mi.
July 23, 1939
Kimelman (U.S.S.R.), 212 mi.

DISTANCE (TWO PLACE)*				
International	*U.S.A.*	*Great Britain*	*France*	*Germany*
Oct. 21, 1936 Ilchencho-Loguin (U.S.S.R.), 83 mi.	July 28, 1936 Slatter-Batterson, 25 mi.			
Apr. 12, 1937 Kneis-Beck (G.), 121 mi.				Apr. 12, 1937 Kneis and Beck, 121 mi.
May 27, 1937 Ilchencho-Emerik (U.S.S.R.), 253 mi.				
May 15, 1938 Ilchencho-Zelenkova (U.S.S.R.), 345 mi.	June 29, 1938 Smith-de Medo, 28 mi.			
July 17, 1938 Kartacheff-Savtzov (U.S.S.R.), 385 mi.	April, 1939 Essery-Hepburn, 43 mi.			

DISTANCE AND RETURN (TWO PLACE)

International	*U.S.A.*	*Great Britain*	*France*	*Germany*
July 28, 1939 Kartacheff-Chechoulkine (U.S.S.R.), 212 mi.				

ALTITUDE (TWO PLACE)*

International	*U.S.A.*	*Great Britain*	*France*	*Germany*
May 3, 1937 Spilger-Hahenne (G.), 7,283 ft.	June 28, 1936 Slatter-Batterson, 5967 ft			May 3, 1937 Spilger-Hahenne, 7,283 ft.
Sept. 18, 1937 Ziller-Quadfasel (G.), 10,840 ft.	July 4, 1939 Barringer-Rodenburg, 6558 ft.			Sept. 18, 1937 Ziller-Quadfasel, 10,840 ft.

* Two-place records were not officially accepted by the F.A.I. until 1936.

July 4, 1936
Slatter-Buxton, 8:48

July, 1937
Fox-Murray
(G.B.), 9:48
Nov. 26, 1937
Jachtmann-Klossdork
(G.), 13:59
Apr. 9, 1938
Makaroff-Godovikoff
(U.S.S.R.), 19:08
Sept. 5-6, 1938
Kahlbacker-Tauschegg
(G.), 23:41
Sept. 9-10, 1938
Fuhringer-Kahlbacker
(G.), 40:38
Dec. 9-11, 1938
Boedecker-Zander (G.),
50:26

July, 1937
Fox-Murray
9:48
July 9-10, 1938
Murray-Sproule, 22:13

Nov. 26-27, 1937
Jachtmann-Klossdork
13:59
Sept. 5-6, 1938
Kahlbacker-Tauschegg,
23:41
Sept. 9-10, 1938
Fuhringer-Kahlbacker,
40:38
Dec. 9-11, 1938
Boedecker-Zander, 50:26

DISTANCE AND RETURN (TWO PLACE)

June 14, 1938
Kartacher-Naoumor
(U.S.S.R.), 12 mi.
Aug. 10, 1938
Huth-Brandt (G.), 186
mi.

Aug. 10, 1938
Huth-Brandt, 186 mi.

* Two-place records were not officially accepted by the F.A.I. until 1936.

WOMEN'S RECORDS

	International	U.S.A.	Great Britain	France	Germany
DISTANCE	July 4, 1937 Reitsch (G.), 218 mi. July 6, 1939 Klepikova (U.S.S.R.), 465 mi.			Apr. 18, 1938 Jarlaud, 52 mi.	July 4, 1937 Reitsch, 218 mi.
ALTITUDE	Apr. 18, 1938 Jarlaud (F.), 3848 ft. July 10, 1939 Zelenkova (U.S.S.R.), 6795 ft.			Apr. 18, 1938 Jarlaud, 3848 ft.	
DURATION	May 13-14, 1937 Modlibowska (Poland), 24:14	June, 1935 duPont, 5:15 Sept. 4, 1938 Montgomery, 7:28		Sept. 22, 1938 Girud, 6:52	
DISTANCE AND RETURN	May 15, 1938 Reitsch (G.), 155 mi.				May 15, 1938 Reitsch, 155 mi.
DISTANCE (TWO PLACE)	July 23, 1939 Velikosseltzeva-Gorokhova (U.S.S.R.), 139 mi.				
ALTITUDE (TWO PLACE)	July 10, 1939 Velikosseltzeva-Gorokhova (U.S.S.R.), 5361 ft.				
DURATION (TWO PLACE)	May 16, 1939 Zelenkova-Samarina (U.S.S.R.), 12:30				

BRIEF BIOGRAPHICAL SKETCHES OF THE FIRST TEN AMERICAN
"SILVER C" PILOTS

(Numbers refer first to U. S. and then to international series.)

Fred T. Loomis

1. J. K. O'MEARA—12

Jack O'Meara, the first American to obtain the coveted "Silver C," was also the first to soar at Elmira, on July 2, 1930. His pioneering flights and efforts helped to bring about the first National Soaring Contest held there the following year. He was born at Bradford, Pennsylvania, June 18, 1909, studied aeronautical engineering at Carnegie Institute of Technology.

In 1932 O'Meara established an American distance record of 66 miles from Elmira to Wyalusing, Pennsylvania. At this same contest at which he became the American Soaring Champion, he also set an altitude record of 4960 feet with his Darmstadt Sailplane "Chanute" which was built by him. After a lapse of several years he again took an active part in the ninth National Contest in 1938 in which he placed fifth after making flights of 115 and 133 miles in the Bowlus "Baby Albatross" intermediate sailplane. He lives in Minneapolis, Minn.

Fred T. Loomis

2. RICHARD C. DU PONT—32

Few, if any, men have done more to help promote American soaring than Richard du Pont. Born in Wilmington, Delaware, on January 2, 1911, he had his first gliding training on Cape Cod in a home-made glider in 1929. Soon afterwards he also became an accomplished airplane pilot and rose to national soaring prominence in 1933 when he set a distance record of 122 miles from Waynesboro, Virginia, to Frederick, Maryland, in his Bowlus-du Pont sailplane, "Albatross I." In 1934 he won his "Silver C," first became National Soaring Champion, and established a national and international distance record of 158 miles from Elmira, New York, to Basking Ridge, New Jersey. On another flight he set an altitude record of 6233 feet, both records standing in America for the next four years. He was American Soaring Champion again in 1935 and 1937. At the ninth Annual Contest in 1938 he broke his own altitude record with a flight to 6804 feet in his Minimoa sailplane in which he also made a flight of 155 miles to Lancaster, Pennsylvania.

President of the Soaring Society of America from 1935 to 1940, he has given unstintingly of his time and finances to promote motorless flying, one of his greatest contributions being the founding of the magazine *Soaring*. At the present time he is President of All American Aviation, Inc., and lives at Granogue, Delaware.

3. LEWIN B. BARRINGER—65

Fred T. Loomis

Born at Wayne, Pennsylvania, on December 17, 1906, the author of this book has had a great interest in aviation since his early youth. He learned to fly airplanes in 1929 and has been a Commercial Pilot ever since. From 1930-1932 he operated the Wings Gliding School at Wings Field, Ambler, Pennsylvania. In 1933 he joined the Pennsylvania National Guard as Second Lieutenant and won his Army Pilot rating. He did his first soaring at the National Contest in 1934 when he flew the Bowlus-du Pont "Albatross II" at the invitation of Richard du Pont. With it he made a flight of 78 miles and 4834 feet. He completed the requirements for his "Silver C" in Virginia that fall on a 5-hour, 15-minute flight from Big Meadows to Front Royal. On April 3, 1935, again flying the "Albatross II," he made the longest ridge soaring flight on record, 154 miles, from Ellenville, New York, to Pikestown, Pennsylvania. The next two years he spent in Iran flying an airplane for an archeological expedition. During 1937 and 1938 he served as General Manager of the Soaring Society of America and Editor of *Soaring*. On April 19, 1938, he established an American distance and goal flight record of 212 miles from Wichita Falls, Texas, to Tulsa, Oklahoma. On July 4, 1939, he established a 2-seater distance altitude record of 6558 feet. He is a Director of the Soaring Society of America.

Dey

4. STANLEY W. SMITH—236

A native of Lydonville, New York, Stanley Smith was born on February 26, 1910. He learned to fly at the Glider Club of the University of Michigan where he was graduated as an aeronautical engineer in 1934. He was National Soaring Champion in 1933 and won his "Silver C" in 1936 with a Rhönbuzzard with distance of 34.5 miles, having completed the altitude and duration requirements with a Franklin utility in previous years. His altitude was 5463 feet and his duration 8 hours, 10 minutes. In 1935 he assisted with the design of the du Pont utility glider. In 1937 he designed and supervised the construction of the two-place utility glider, "City of Utica" at the New York Aviation School in Utica which he supervised for two years. He was President of the U. of M. Glider Club in 1934 and a Director of the SSA in 1935 and 1936. In 1938 he bettered the American distance record with passenger by flying the "City of Utica" 28 miles. He is now in the Engineering Department of the Bell Aircraft Corporation, Buffalo, New York.

Charles S. Hoffmeier

5. EMIL A. LEHECKA—237

Emil Lehecka is one of the outstanding aerobatic pilots in the United States. He was born on June 9, 1914, at Long Island City,

New York, and showed an early interest in flying. An airplane as well as a glider pilot, he is also senior instructor of the Airhoppers Gliding and Soaring Club of New York City. He won his "Silver C" at the National Contest in 1936 flying his Cadet utility specially stressed for aerobatics. In 1937 he imported a Rhönsperber sailplane and with it tied for third place in the contest with best distance of 118 miles. With this ship he won the American Soaring Championship in 1938 with consistent effort and best flights of 5300 feet and 130 miles. He is a Director of the Soaring Society of America.

6. HENRY N. WIGHTMAN
—238

Newark Sunday Call

Born at New Windsor, New York, on June 10, 1913, Henry Wightman received his gliding training from the author at the Wings Gliding School in 1931. He continued his flying as a member of the University of Michigan Glider Club while a student at that university. For several years he has won the annual contest of the Associated Glider Clubs of New Jersey. He qualified for his "Silver C" at the National Soaring Contest in 1936 during which he made a remarkable and so far unequaled flight with the du Pont utility glider of 138 miles to Middletown, New York, during which he reached a maximum altitude of 5980 feet. His endurance requirement was made at the 1935 Contest with a flight of 6 hours, 45 minutes. He was graduated from college with a degree in aeronautical engineering in 1938 and in 1939 was General Manager of the Soaring Society of America and Editor of *Soaring*.

7. EMERSON MEHLHOSE
—239

Emerson Mehlhose was born on July 27, 1913, in Wyandotte, Michigan. As early as 1928 he was president of the Glider Club of Roosevelt High School. After graduation he built a utility glider which competed successfully in the National Soaring Contests from 1933 to 1936, under the colors of the Lawrence Institute of Technology. On his first soaring flight at Uniontown, Pennsylvania, in 1932, he attained an altitude of 4000 feet above the valley on evening thermals. In 1933 he soared a distance of 71 miles from Waynesboro to Front Royal, Virginia, just exceeding the U. S. distance record of 66 miles.

In 1934 at the National Soaring Contest he made a flight of 8 hours' duration. In 1936, flying a Haller "Hawk" to 6515 feet, he exceeded the altitude record. At the present time he is President of the Wyandotte Soaring Club.

8. CHESTER J. DECKER·
—240

Chester Decker, a native of Brooklyn, New York, was born on October 18, 1914. At Glen Rock, New Jersey, his present home, he built several gliders of his own design in 1934 and flew them at Warwick, New York. In 1935 he first competed at Elmira with a Franklin utility and won the title of Outstanding Junior Pilot. That year he made a duration flight of 7 hours, 5 minutes. The following year, flying the Bowlus-du Pont sailplane, "Albatross I," the greatest distance of the contest (146 miles), he became American Soaring Champion. The altitude requirement for his "Silver C" was also made that year with a flight to 5500 feet. In 1937 he tied for second place with Emil Lehecka. In 1938 flying a Minimoa he placed third with best flight of 175 miles. In 1939 he again became national champion and America's third "Golden C" Pilot. He is President of the North Jersey Soaring Association and Treasurer of the Soaring Society of America.

9. HARLAND C. ROSS—510

Cy La Tour

A native of Alva, Oklahoma, where he was born on March 4, 1906, Harland Ross has lived mostly in Wichita Falls, Texas. Graduating from the Wichita Falls Junior College in May 1926, he soon showed a great interest in motorless flying, but was practically unknown to national soaring until his appearance at the 1937 contest with the high performance Ross-Stephens sailplane designed and built by him. With it, Ross, an airplane as well as sailplane pilot, won his "Silver C" and fifth place in the contest. His duration was 5 hours, 42 minutes, his altitude 4000 feet, and his distance, second best in the contest, was 121 miles. In 1938, flying a converted secondary with wing of his own design, he reached an unofficial altitude record of 7000 feet at Wichita Falls. He is now employed by the Lockheed Aircraft Company and lives in Burbank, California, where he designs and builds sailplanes in his spare time.

10. Arthur B. Schultz—511

The leader of motorless flying in the Detroit area and past President of the Detroit Glider Council, Arthur Schultz was born in Schenectady, New York, February 1, 1904. In 1927 he was graduated as an aeronautical engineer from the University of Michigan. In 1930 he joined the ABC Glider Club, earned his "C" license No. 22 at Elmira the following year, and in 1935 with his partner John Nowak discovered and pioneered the soaring possibilities of the sand dunes near Empire and Frankfort, Michigan, which resulted in the Annual Midwest Soaring Contest. Combined with the 1938 American Open Contest it ranked second in 1938 only to the National Soaring Contest at Elmira. He designed and built the ABC intermediate sailplane which won the Eaton Design Competition in 1937. With it he won his "Silver C" license that year with 7 hours, 7 minutes, 4210 feet and 51 miles. In 1939 he designed the Midwest sailplane which has shown very fine performance. He is employed in Detroit as an engineer designing marine engines and is a Director of The Soaring Society of America.

ADDITIONAL
AMERICAN "SILVER C" PILOTS

U. S. No.	Name	International No.	Distance	Altitude	Duration
11	Warren Merboth	871	98 mi.	4115 ft.	5 hrs. 18 min.
12	Robert Stanley	872	122 mi.	6380 ft.	6 hrs. 8 min.
13	Stanley Corcoran	873	183 mi.	4040 ft.	6 hrs. 23 min.
14	Theodore Bellak	874	45 mi.	5603 ft.	5 hrs. 5 min.
15	Robert Auburn	875	78 mi.	5390 ft.	6 hrs. 8 min.
16	Julian Hadley	876	38 mi.	5200 ft.	5 hrs. 22 min.
17	Floyd Sweet	877	133 mi.	5580 ft.	5 hrs. 56 min.
18	John Robinson	——*	42 mi.	3600 ft.	5 hrs. 25 min.
19	Udo Fischer	——	60 mi.	6070 ft.	9 hrs. 36 min.
20	Elmer Zook	——	53 mi.	4600 ft.	10 hrs. 55 min.
21	Harland McHenry	——	38 mi.	4520 ft.	6 hrs. 19 min.
22	Harvey Stephens	——	195 mi.	4400 ft.	5 hrs. 50 min.
23	Donald Stevens	——	38 mi.	4260 ft.	5 hrs. 10 min.
24	Parker Leonard	——	52 mi.	4500 ft.	7 hrs. 1 min.

AMERICAN "GOLDEN C" PILOTS

1	Robert Stanley	——*	219 mi.	17,264 ft.
2	Chester Decker	——	233 mi.	10,165 ft.
3	John Robinson	——	200 mi.	11,550 ft.

* International numbers not yet assigned due to war delays.

BRITISH "SILVER C" PILOTS

(British number before each pilot's name, and the international number after it.)

1934
1. G. E. Collins — 26
2. P. A. Wills — 45

1935
3. R. G. Robertson — 75
4. S. Humphries — 85
5. J. C. Neilan — 174
6. C. Nicholson — 177
7. Miss N. Heron-Maxwell — 208

1936
8. P. M. Watt — 241
9. H. C. Bergel — 244
10. A. L. Slater — 291
11. G. O. Smith — 298

1937
12. J. S. Fox — 338
13. R. S. Rattray — 542
14. P. B. N. Davis — 543
15. G. H. Stephenson — 545
16. D. G. O. Hiscox — 560
17. K. G. Wilkinson — 561
18. J. E. Simpson — 562
19. J. V. Rushton — 563

BRITISH "GOLDEN C" PILOTS

1. Philip Wills — 4

20.	G. A. Little	564
21.	K. Lingford	565
22.	J. S. Sproule	566
23.	K. W. Turner	567
24.	E. J. Furlong	568
25.	S. C. O'Grady	585
26.	E. E. H. Collins	594
27.	J. L. Wordsworth	595
28.	Mrs. J. Price	621
29.	G. M. Thompson	622
30.	L. R.. Robertson	625

1938

31.	E. Thomas	856
32.	I. Pasold	857
33.	H. Tudor Edmunds	858
34.	J. C. Dent	859
35.	L. H. Barker	860
36.	D. F. Greig	861
37.	A. J. Deane-Drummond	1004
38.	A. Ivanoff	1005
39.	A. W. Lacey	1006
40.	M. H. Maufe	1007
41.	J. Parker	1008
42.	E. H. Taylor	1009
43.	K. M. Chirgwin	1061
44.	R. Pasold	1062
45.	J. W. S. Pringle	1063
46.	J. A. Rooper	1064
47.	J. H. Saffery	1093
48.	P. M. Thomas	1094
49.	G. L. Raphael	1095
50.	A. Davies	1096

TOTAL "SILVER C's" WON IN DIFFERENT COUNTRIES BETWEEN
APRIL 15, 1931, AND DECEMBER 31, 1938

Germany	816
Poland	159
England	50
France	29
Switzerland	19
United States	17
Hungary	9
Jugo-Slavia	4
Finland	3
Holland	3
Czechoslovakia	3
Brazil	1
Sweden	1
Rumania	1
Egypt	1
Lithuania	1
	1117

"GOLDEN C" PILOTS

Int. Number	Name	Address
1.	Heini Dittmar	Darmstadt
2.	Hermann Zitter	Darmstadt
3.	Philip Wills	London
4.	Eric Nessler	Paris
5.	Heinz Peters	Wasserkuppe
6.	Rudolf Opitz	Darmstadt
7.	Wolfgang Spate	Darmstadt
8.	Karl Schieferstein	Darmstadt
9.	Heinrich Huth	Hamburg-Fuhlsbuttel
10.	Arno Kuhnold	Laucha
11.	Peter van Husen	Grunau
12.	Kurt Schmidt	Munchen
13.	Otto Braeutigam	Gr. Ruckerswaldé
14.	Franz Pomper	Konigsberg
15.	Rudolf Steinert	Poppitz Sa
16.	Gunther Lemm	Berlin
17.	Ernst-Gunther Haase	Dortmund
18.	Gerhard Sauerbier	Breslau
19.	Oblt. Flakowski	Merseburg
20.	Heinz Schubert	Darmstadt
21.	Werner Fick	Perleberg
22.	Gotthold Peter	Berlin
23.	Karl Treuter	Jena
24.	Hermann Winter	Johannesburg, South Africa

BIBLIOGRAPHY

(This list does not include all the books on the subject, but only the best and most useful for the student of motorless flight.)

American Books

Gliders and Gliding, Lt. Com. Ralph S. Barnaby. Ronald Press, New York, 1930.

Gliding and Soaring Manual. (Official manual of The Soaring Society of America.) Stone Aircraft Co., Box 57, Detroit, Mich., 1939.

English Books

Gliding and Sailplaning: A Beginner's Handbook, F. Stamer and A. Lippisch (translated from German). John Lane, The Bodley Head, Ltd., London, 1930.

Sailplanes: Their Design, Construction and Pilotage, C. H. Latimer Needham. Chapman and Hall, Ltd., London, 1937.

Kronfeld on Gliding and Soaring, Robert Kronfeld. John Hamilton, Ltd., London, 1932.

German Books

The Art of Soaring Flight, Wolf Hirth (translated from German). Stuttgarter Vereinsbuchdruckerei AG., Stuttgart, 1938.

Handbuch des Segelfliegens, Wolf Hirth. Franch'sche Verlagshandlung, Stuttgart, 1938.

Die Praxis des Leistungs-Segelfliegens, Erich Bachem. C. J. E. Volckmann Nachf., Berlin-Charlottenburg, 1936.

Periodicals

Soaring (monthly). The Soaring Society of America, Inc., P.O. Box 71, Elmira, New York.

The Sailplane and Glider (monthly). H. O. Davies, 13, Victoria St., London, S.W.1, England.

Amicale du Vol à Voile Français (monthly). Aero Club de France, 6, rue Galilée, Paris, France.

Flugsport (bi-monthly). Hindenburgplatz 8, Frankfurt a.M., Germany.

Samolet (monthly). Moscow, U.S.S.R.

GLOSSARY

Aerobatics—Acrobatic maneuvers in flight, such as loops, rolls, etc.

Aileron—Movable surface for lateral control, forming part of outer, rear portion of wing.

Airfoil—Cross-section design of wing or lifting surface.

Angle of attack—Angle between chord line of wing and level line of flight of fuselage.

Aspect ratio—Ratio of span to mean chord of wing.

Bank—Lateral inclination of glider while turning in flight.

Burble—An eddy in an airflow.

Cabane—A structure on top of glider fuselage forming support for wings.

Cantilever—A wing having its supporting structure within itself.

Centroid—A geometric property of a beam, spar member, etc., used in strength calculations. It is the center of area.

Chord—The width of a wing measured from leading edge to trailing edge.

Crack-up—An accident involving serious structural damage to a glider.

Dep control—Control stick with wheel for lateral control. Named for Deperdussin, the Frenchman who invented it.

Dihedral—Angle between horizontal line drawn laterally from center of bottom side of wing and line formed by the wing inclined upwards.

Dope—A nitro-cellulose fluid used to tighten and protect fabric-covered surfaces of a glider.

D-tube—Structure formed by combination of spar and curved metal or plywood leading edge of wing.

Drag—Retarding force due to aerodynamic resistance.

Elevator—Hinged, horizontal tail surface for controlling glider in the vertical plane.

Empennage—The tail of the glider, including horizontal and vertical stabilizing and control surfaces.

Fairing—Structure added to glider for streamlining or lessening of drag.

Fairleads—Leading of control cable to prevent cutting or chafing.

Fin—Fixed, vertical tail surface for longitudinal stability.

Fishtail—A sideways, level, alternately skidding maneuver to decrease excessive flying speed close to the ground.

Flaps—Movable surfaces hinged to rear portion of wing to facilitate approaches to landings by increasing lift and drag.

Fuselage—The body of the glider.

Gliding ratio—Ratio of distance covered horizontally to height lost vertically.

Gross weight—Weight of glider fully loaded with pilot and equipment.

Gusset—A triangular piece of plywood or metal fastened across a structural joint to increase stiffness and strength.

Horn—Fixed projection on control surface providing leverage action for control cable or tube.

Idler—An idler horn, pushrod, gear, etc., is a member of a system used to change direction, rotation, or to facilitate connections.

Jig—A fixed form or mold to facilitate exact fabrication and duplication of parts.

Longeron—Principal longitudinal structural members of a fuselage.

Monocoque—A type of fuselage construction the strength of which is largely in a metal or plywood shell due to its round or oval design.

Nose—The front of the glider's fuselage.

Placard—Prominent notice painted on side of glider fuselage.

Radio-sonde—A radio meteorgraph; an instrument sent aloft (50,000 to 100,000 feet) on a balloon, sending out continuous signals of soundings of temperature, altitude and relative humidity which are picked up and automatically plotted on paper by a machine on the ground.

Release—Mechanism in nose of glider holding ring at the end of towline until tripped by pilot.

Rudder—Vertical, hinged tail surface for directional control in horizontal plane.

Sinking speed—The rate of vertical descent while gliding.

Skid (noun)—Curved, wooden runner under fuselage forming part of landing gear.

Skid (verb)—A sideways, slipping maneuver resulting from overcontrol of the rudder.

Slip—A maneuver where the glider loses height sideways in the direction of the down wing while banked.

Span—The distance between the wing tips of a glider.

Spar—Beam used as principal structural unit of wing.

Spoiler—Small, hinged control surface on upper side of wing to decrease lift and increase drag to steepen glide path in landing.

Stabilizer—Fixed, horizontal tail surface for stability in vertical plane.

Stall—A loss of lift due to insufficient air speed over the wing.

Stringer—A light, longitudinal structural member to stiffen a fuselage.

Strut—A bar or rod used as an outside structural member of a glider.

Tailplane—Horizontal tail surface including stabilizer and elevators.

Torque—A twisting or rotary force.

Towline—Rope, cable, or wire used to tow a glider.

Turnbuckle—A coupling with internal screw threads for regulating the tension of a wire or cable.

Washout—Decreased angle of attack of wings toward tips.

ABBREVIATIONS

B.G.A.—British Gliding Association

C.A.A.—Civil Aeronautics Authority (U.S.A.)

C.A.R.—Civil Air Regulations

D.L.V.—Deutsch Luftsport Verband

N.A.A.—National Aeronautic Association

N.A.C.A.—National Advisory Committee for Aeronautics

S.S.A.—Soaring Society of America

INDEX